Blink of an Eye

Louisa Scarr studied Psychology at the University of Southampton and has lived in and around the city ever since. She works as a freelance copywriter and editor, and when she's not writing, she can be found pounding the streets in running shoes or swimming in muddy lakes.

Also by Louisa Scarr

Butler & West

Last Place You Look
Under a Dark Cloud
Blink of an Eye

LOUISA SCARR

BLINK OF AN EYE

First published in the United Kingdom in 2022 by

Canelo
Unit 9, 5th Floor
Cargo Works, 1-2 Hatfields
London, SE1 9PG
United Kingdom

A CIP catalogue record for this book is available from the British Library.

Print ISBN 978 1 80032 350 6
Ebook ISBN 978 1 80032 349 0

Look for more great books at www.canelo.co

Printed and bound in Great Britain by Clays Ltd, Elcograf S.p.A.

1

For the original residents of 28 Shakespeare:
Anne, Beef, Div, Meenal, Nikki, Seetal and Sue.

Prologue

He knows what they're going to say. He knew when the man called last night, the voice nervous but efficient. *Yes, tomorrow. No, we can't tell you the results over the phone.*

He sits in the silent waiting room. Alone. He's brought a file from work to look through while he waits but he can't concentrate. His surroundings are shabby; they scream of a lack of budget, of officious suits cutting costs. He wonders how many lives have been ruined here. How many futures destroyed.

The nurse calls him through; he follows her, mute. He sits down next to the doctor, who checks his name, the first line of his address, his date of birth. They don't want to have this conversation with the wrong person, he thinks. Not this sort of news.

The doctor glances at his file, then meets his gaze. His eyes are sad, mouth downturned.

'I'm sorry,' the doctor says. 'Your results aren't what we were hoping for.'

But he already knew.

He knew the moment he went to his GP. He'd felt the exhaustion. Not the usual aches from working long hours at the office, or after running a half-marathon, or clubbing all night. But a weariness deep in his bones that no amount of sleep could shift. The weight loss came after; he didn't feel like eating and his secretary asked, 'Are you okay? You don't look so good.'

The doctor tells him about treatment, and referrals, and chemotherapy, and appointments. He's handed leaflets. Promises made that a nurse from Macmillan will call. Names, dates, job titles that mean nothing now but will become all too familiar.

They finish their conversation. He shakes the doctor's hand and thanks him. For what? he wonders as he walks away. Somehow, he finds his way back to the lift. Dazed. Reeling. The woman next to him queries which floor and for a second he stares at her, dumb, unable to ascertain what she's asking.

He stumbles back to his car, pays the parking ticket, then sits in the driver's seat, keys in his hand.

The car is warm; July sunshine blasts through the metal and glass. Sweat blooms, forming damp patches under his arms. He has never felt more cold.

What now? Work seems wrong. He doesn't want to go home. Sitting alone in his empty house, no one to call.

All he can think is: how long? Long enough to make it to Christmas? Long enough to go abroad? To make the trip to New Zealand he'd always planned?

Long enough to make amends?

The thought spurs him into action. He reaches into his bag and pulls out a blue notebook, one he uses every day for work. He knows what he needs to do. He knows what needs to happen.

With a shaking hand, he writes two lines at the top:

For the attention of Detective Constable Freya West.
Private and Confidential.

Part 1

1

Saturday

Ice crunches underfoot; it's still dark. The bell jangles on the Santa hat hastily forced onto his head by his four-year-old granddaughter. The Labrador shoots off towards the sea as soon as she's released from her lead: a black shadow disappearing into the dawn. He sighs and trudges after her.

His stomach rumbles. He thinks of strong coffee, of toast and smoked salmon, and rich scrambled eggs made with butter and full-cream milk. Treats he is usually denied, but not today. Even his wife will be in a good mood, letting his diet slip in the name of good cheer and celebration.

He hears his dog bark. A rare exclamation from a normally placid creature, and he strains his eyes in the dull light to see what she's doing. She's stopped, her tail alert, her nose pointing; gun dog training coming to the fore. But here, he thinks. Why here?

He walks a few paces, feet stumbling on the loose stones. There are lumps on the beach, an unusual sight that makes his body instinctively hesitate. Two more steps. He can see clothing, shoes.

Someone's dumped rubbish? The dog barks again, then sniffs at the heaps, leaping playfully around them.

He leans forward and tugs the Labrador away to look closer.

Then, with a frantic gasp, he pulls out his phone and dials 999.

2

Robin waits for the impact, his body tense. He'd felt the brakes fail, the futile turn of the steering wheel as his old Volvo continued its course unimpeded. Metal hits metal – a grind and a screech, and the car comes to a halt.

He puts on the handbrake, then opens the door with a slow, resigned sigh. He hadn't been going fast but he knows he won't like what he's about to see as he walks with small hesitant steps to the front of his car.

Long scratches run across the bumper and then down the side, the bright yellow from the pole embedded in the bodywork. The pole itself hasn't moved, stubbornly still advertising the Long Stay Car Park. Freezing air bites immediately at the tip of Robin's nose; wind grabs at his clothes as he zips his coat up against the bitter cold, pulling his scarf over his chin. He leans down and pulls ineffectually at the broken bumper.

'Bollocks,' he mutters.

He stands up straight and surveys the scene. A long mirror of ice coats the car park; a puddle frozen solid overnight. A few vehicles stand side by side, windscreens misty-white with frost. Others, arrived that morning, are parked off to the left, bumpers intact, sensibly avoiding the slick Robin has fallen victim to.

In the distance he can see blue lights flashing. He waits as they get closer, two ambulances trundling towards him and passing, heading towards the main road. The survivors, he assumes, wondering at the extent of their injuries. But one body remains. He knows that much.

He takes a quick photo on his phone of his car *in situ*, debating if it's even worth the insurance claim, then pops the boot, awkwardly taking his trainers off and pulling thick socks and wellingtons on his feet. He walks towards the crime scene.

Rows of picture-perfect beach huts in turquoise and green and yellow offset against the bright blue sky. He trudges away from the road, concrete giving way to rough stones. Grey waves lap on the shore. White foam, brown wooden groynes. Copper pebbles on light yellow sand.

People come into view. Uniformed officers in black and fluorescent yellow; white crime scene suits. A blue-and-white ribboned cordon has been constructed around red traffic cones and it pulls, rippling in the wind. In the middle of it all: the body.

He shows his ID to the scene guard.

'Detective Sergeant Robin Butler. Major Crimes.'

He's waved through; he suits up quickly in the usual overalls, and a finger points him towards the smaller person crouched next to the body. He recognises her, even with the padded layers underneath her suit giving her a much bulkier silhouette than usual. Dr Steph Harper. Forensic pathologist, friend. Some might even say ex-girlfriend if they were being generous about last year's occasional hook-ups and week-long attempt at a proper relationship. She stands as she sees him approaching and pulls the mask down from her face.

'Merry Christmas, Robin,' she says with a smile.

'Morning,' he replies. 'What has Santa brought us?'

'Dead bloke. Not his usual sort of present.' She gestures towards the body. 'Do you want to see?'

He crouches down next to her, knee joints cracking.

'Male,' Steph begins. 'Driving licence found in his pocket confirms him as Alexander Reynolds, forty-three years old.' The evidence bag is handed over and Robin squints at the face on the photo, then compares it to the dead man. In real life he's thinner and paler, a blue woolly hat on his head, but it's him, that's for sure.

'The others left in the ambulances?' Robin asks.

Steph nods. 'Five in total. Two women, two other men. All regained consciousness quickly after the dog walker discovered them, except for the one closest to the water's edge. He was still out when the ambulances took them.'

'Where to?'

'The General. My guess is the prognosis for those three will be fine. Walking wounded. Maybe a bit of hypothermia. I wouldn't like to say about the unconscious bloke.'

'What were they doing out here?' Robin wonders aloud. 'It must have been Baltic last night.' He looks at the debris remaining on the beach. He counts four empty cans of what Robin assumes to be a sickly-sweet strawberry cocktail, a variety of blankets. A big thermos, the lid on its side nearby. A small silver hip flask next to the body. A mottled-glass bottle of vodka – the expensive sort – and one of Famous Grouse whisky. Both large bottles, both empty.

'Quite the party,' he comments.

'The SOCOs are on their way,' Steph replies. 'They'll get this lot bagged up for you.' She turns back to the dead man. 'The hospital will take bloods on our injured parties, run some tests. And I'll do the same on this guy. There's no obvious cause of death. Bar the fact it was below zero last night.'

'Thanks, Steph. And you say it was a dog walker that discovered them?'

She points towards the man sitting behind them in the doorway of a navy-blue beach hut. A black Labrador sits at his feet.

'God bless the dog walkers,' Steph says. 'How would we find the dead bodies without them?'

–

Robin walks up the shingle towards the man. The Labrador gets up to greet him, slobbery jaws full of sand and bits of wood. Robin pulls his crime scene suit off then tugs his beanie on his head, his gloves back on his already numb hands.

'Sorry to disturb your Christmas,' Robin begins, taking in the bright red Santa hat. 'If you could answer a few questions, then I can let you get on your way.'

'Of course. It's not a problem,' the man says. The dog collapses at his feet, turning its attention to the piece of driftwood it's been gnawing. 'Someone else's day is going to be considerably worse, after all.'

Robin nods. Christmas morning, and a policeman's going to turn up on someone's doorstep, telling them that their son, brother, maybe even husband, is dead. The thought crosses his mind that the unfortunate copper is probably him.

'Can you take me through what happened?' he asks.

'Not much. We walk here most mornings, Cassie and I.' The dog, Robin gathers. 'And at this time, in this weather, we're normally alone. But today she found those bodies. At least, I assumed they were bodies. But then she licked a few of them and they opened their eyes. Poor sods, they were freezing. I called 999, then gave them whatever clothing I had. A few blankets out of the car.'

'Did they tell you much? Say what they were doing?'

'No. They were all shocked. Especially when two of them didn't wake up.'

'And what time was this?'

'Just after seven. My granddaughter woke us all at six' – he gives a weary smile – 'so I took Cassie out for some peace and quiet.'

'Did you see anyone else? Nearby, or as you were walking this way?'

He shakes his head. 'No, no one. Is that guy dead?' he asks, pointing back to the scene.

'I'm afraid so, yes.'

'Oh. Sad.' His attention is diverted for a moment. Then something occurs to him. 'One of them was the wife of the unconscious guy. The rest were friends, I think.'

'What gave you that impression?'

'Just the way they were with each other. Familiar. Worried. I saw the empty bottles. Were they all drinking?'

'I'm guessing so, yes. Have you noticed anything similar around here before?'

'A bit in the summer,' he replies, 'but not this time of year, no. Funny place to come. In this weather.' His phone rings and he pulls it out of his pocket. 'My wife,' he says to Robin with a grimace. 'She'll be wanting to know where I am.'

He smiles. 'Tell her you're on your way home. I'll be in touch if I need anything else. Thank you.'

The man answers his call and, with the dog trotting happily at his side, he heads off. Robin watches him go, hat at a jaunty angle, and imagines the rest of this man's day. In a warm house, with family and food and presents. Nothing even remotely similar to what he has to look forward to.

Robin starts to walk away, along the edge of the beach, assessing the surroundings. It's quiet; low voices carry over from where the body lies, the caw of seagulls, the lapping of waves on the stones. There's the smell of seaweed and salt in the air; in the distance the Red Funnel ferry glides towards the Isle of Wight. He speeds up, putting some exertion into his freezing legs, and he feels his body grow warm under his thick jacket.

He'd woken alone, in a silent house. No decorations, no presents. No smile or kiss on the cheek. He hasn't even bothered to put a tree up because what would be the point? Who would it be for?

He has no family: his parents are dead, his sister gone. The only person that could be described as such – Liam, his brother-in-law – is at his own parents'. He'd asked Robin to join him, but Robin had declined: being an interloper to all that love is worse somehow. A reminder of everything he's missing.

He looks back to the crime scene, thinking. The SOCOs are here now, two white suits taking stock of what exhibits to collect. It's a strange place to go to on Christmas Eve. To bring drinks and alcohol to the water's edge, when freezing temperatures and a bitter wind were forecast. When, he assumes, they all had warm homes to make use of instead. And how had they all ended up unconscious?

He sees another figure appear: a stocky Black bloke, his already considerable size emphasised by the red ski jacket he's wearing. People stand up, taking notice of his arrival, his authority clear even from this distance. He turns in Robin's direction; Robin raises a hand, then starts walking towards him.

'Guv,' Robin says when they're close. 'You didn't need to come. Isn't there another DI on call?'

'Glad to. Chandice is staying and she's driving me nuts.'

Robin laughs. DCI Neal Baker is over six foot and almost as wide. An ex-boxer, it's hard to imagine him taking shit from anyone, although it seems his mother-in-law is the exception.

'You're thinking category one?' Baker asks.

A sudden death involving a suspected offence. 'Until we know otherwise,' Robin confirms.

'Partying that got out of hand?'

'Maybe. Drugs, on top of the alcohol? Although god knows why. Here, of all places.'

'Have you interviewed them yet?'

'Going to head to the hospital now.'

'Good. And call West.' Robin doesn't reply and Baker gives him a long look. 'Seriously, Butler. You can't do three interviews by yourself. Give me an update later.'

Robin watches him go, then pulls his phone out of his pocket. He stamps his feet, trying to get some feeling back into his numb toes.

She answers on the second ring. Her voice is muffled and confused.

'Freya? I'm sorry, but I need you.'

A muffled groan; a male voice in the background. 'Yeah, sure,' she says, sleepily. 'Tell me where.'

He tells her and hangs up. A small part of him – well, maybe not so small – enjoys having an excuse to spend today with Freya. If he is going to be miserable on Christmas Day, it's good to have company. He reaches down and picks up a handful of pebbles, running them through his gloved fingers. No, he tells himself. He won't drag it out. He'll stay if need be, but they'll do the bare minimum together, a first pass at the hospital, then he'll let Freya go back to her life. To her *boyfriend*.

He drops the last pebble, then spots a small whelk shell. He bends down to pick it up. He rubs the sand away with a finger, cleaning off the pale pink whorls, worn almost soft in the sea. It's unbroken, perfectly formed.

He hears a shout and sees Steph waving from the crime scene. He heads back over.

'I'm done here,' Steph says, once he's next to her. 'I'll arrange for the body to be transported.'

Robin nods a hello to Jess, the Crime Scene Manager, and sees with satisfaction that the belongings have been bagged up, ready to be taken to the lab for analysis. If there are drugs, they'll find them.

'What have you got there?' Steph asks, referring to the shell he's still working round in his fingers.

Robin looks at it. He thinks of the presents that Alexander Reynolds won't unwrap that morning; of the uncertain fragility of life, even down to the tiny creature that used to live in this shell.

He holds the whelk out to her, and she takes it.

'Merry Christmas, Steph,' he says with a smile.

3

Freya sighs and replaces her mobile phone on the bedside table with a fumbling hand; she hears a muffled thump as it drops to the carpet. She rolls onto her back and stares at the ceiling.

A heavy arm flops across her stomach; a mop of messy dark hair moves next to hers on the pillow.

'I've been called in,' Freya says.

Josh lifts his head and regards her with heavy-lidded eyes. 'Butler couldn't manage by himself for one day?'

'It's a G28, category one. One dead, one unconscious. Another three taken to hospital.'

'I'll let him off then.' Josh's head drops and he rolls onto his side, facing away from her. 'Where were they found?' he asks after a pause.

Freya smiles; she knew his professional curiosity wouldn't allow him to resist for long. 'Calshot beach,' she replies. She tucks her body next to him, her knees behind his. A few more minutes won't hurt, she thinks, sleepily. She drapes her arm over him; his hand finds hers and she feels him kiss her fingers.

'Fucking freezing last night,' he murmurs. His voice is morning-husky. 'Do you think you'll be all day? I don't want to miss out on your mum's Christmas dinner.'

She presses her cheek against his back; his skin is soft, normally taut muscles relaxed.

'Go anyway. You know my mum will be happy to have you.'

'Not without you.'

He rolls back towards her, and she rests her head on his chest.

'What will you do?'

'Sleep off this hangover. Make myself a fry-up. Call my parents.' He looks down, his chin crumpled, his blue eyes meeting hers. 'Merry Christmas, Freya,' he says, and kisses her.

'Merry Christmas, Josh.'

–

She reluctantly hauls herself out of bed – the duvet soft, Josh's body warm – and sits on the edge, pushing the heels of her hands into her eyes. They went out last night: a trip to the pub with Josh's mates, one glass of wine too many, considering she knew she'd be on call today. But she'd felt happy and optimistic – nobody would die tomorrow, surely? How wrong she could be.

She has a quick shower, but leaves her hair dry and piles it into a messy bun at the nape of her neck. She'll do it properly later; make an effort then, still hoping for some sort of Christmas celebration when her job is done.

She goes down to her kitchen and, while she quickly eats a bowl of muesli, she thinks about how unexpected the last six months have been. Her initial reticence to go out with someone from work – and someone with Josh's reputation – had faded quickly. A few dates, meals out, evenings to the pub, and he'd been chivalrous, fun. Gentle. She'd told him early on that her last boyfriend had died, and he'd never tried to push it, letting her take the lead.

It had been worth the wait. Sex with Josh is bloody brilliant. From that first time – cautious, missionary, self-conscious – to last night's slightly drunken, quick bang in the hallway, she has done nothing but crave him naked. He is fit. Broad shoulders, nice arse. *Hot.*

But it isn't just that. Oh, fuck, how she loves him. Since she'd found herself watching him at work – talking, laughing with one of their colleagues – she'd felt the butterflies take hold in her stomach. She'd known. She loves him with a fierceness that scares the shit out of her. It terrifies her to the point she veers between wanting to spend every second wrapped around him in a cocoon, to pushing him away in case one day she loses him like she lost Jonathan. It isn't rational, it isn't sensible. After Jon, she swore never to fall for someone again. And definitely not with this bloke. A man who knows the backstory to Marvel films like it's a religion, who rolls up his trousers and paddles in the sea, even in winter. Who has long legs and soft feet that poke out of the bottom of the duvet when he sleeps. Not this man, surely?

But she has. And fallen hard.

It'll be okay, she tells herself. She stands up, putting her empty bowl into the dishwasher. She has boundaries. This is her house – even though he's always here, rather than his crappy, shared flat. It's only been six months; she can live without him. But as she closes her front door with a quiet click, as she passes his VW Golf on her drive, she feels a warm glow thinking about him upstairs. In her bed. It's all she can do not to turn round and go back up to join him.

She's kidding herself, and she knows it.

She's in deep.

It had been below zero last night, coating her little Fiat 500 in a white, solid frost. She hurriedly scrapes at the worst of it. Air blows furiously from the vents as she drives, demisting her breath on the windscreen. She thrusts one of her gloved hands under her legs in a vain attempt to warm it.

The roads have been cleared, so the drive to the hospital is easy. Few cars litter the spaces on the top floor of the multistorey; she spots Robin's Volvo, parks next to it and heads inside.

She follows the signs towards the Emergency Department, feet crunching on the brown-salted pathways. Even though it's a short walk, her toes and fingers are instantly numb; every breath makes her lungs ache with the bitter cold.

Bright, gawdy decorations have been set up around the reception desk. The woman behind it is wearing a set of brown felt reindeer antlers. They droop over her glasses and she pushes them up, annoyed, as Freya shows her ID.

'Your colleague is over there,' she points. 'Don't get in the way of the doctors.'

Robin's standing to the side of the corridor, facing the entrance to a ward. The sight of him makes her smile fondly. His hair is a mess, due a haircut. Smooth on one side, sharp peaks on the other. His cheeks are pink from the cold. His shoulders are stooped as he stares down towards the rows of beds, no doubt considering what went on last night.

His familiar frown turns into an apologetic smile as she approaches.

'Sorry, Frey,' he says immediately. 'I wouldn't have called, but I can't do the interviews alone.'

She shrugs. 'It's fine, I get it. Fill me in.'

He points down the left-hand side of the ward. 'These three are about to be discharged. Sam Bowen, there, and Meg Carlton and Sara Williams on the right. All had mild hypothermia when they came in, but nothing now except the hangovers. Judging from the bottles at the scene, they were doing some serious drinking last night. Not sure yet if they were on anything else. Sara is married to the guy who's been admitted. Mike Williams.'

'Do we know how he is?'

'I've spoken to the doctor. Severely hypothermic, frostbite to both hands. The tide came in and soaked him. Unlike the others, he wasn't wearing any sort of decent clothing or gloves. Add that to the freezing water and the fact he's a smoker – nicotine slows the body's response to cold,' he continues, seeing Freya about to ask, 'then it's clear why he's in much worse shape than the three here. It was below zero last night, with substantial wind chill. Include the alcohol and the related dehydration, and you have all the risk factors for frostbite.'

Freya grins. 'You're quite the expert this morning,' she comments.

'Doctor was in a sharing mood.'

'But why were they all unconscious?'

'No idea yet. Waiting for toxicology results, hoping they will tell us more. The deceased, Alexander Reynolds, was pronounced dead at the scene—'

'Alex Reynolds?' Freya cuts in. 'Not the solicitor?'

'Er, I'm not sure.' Robin looks down at his phone, no doubt reading the notes he's already obtained from the Police National Computer. 'IC1, slim build, forty-three? Brown hair. Oh, yeah, here it is. Solicitor at Coombes and Rosewood.' He looks up. 'You knew him?'

'I've worked with him a few times. Most recently on the Duncan Thorpe case, last June. The bloke found in the freezer?' Robin nods, and Freya pauses, taking a breath. 'You've met him. He was nice, good at his job. Seemed to care?' Some duty solicitors don't, as Robin well knows. 'And you think his death is suspicious?'

'A forty-three-year-old man found dead on a deserted beach, with only four unconscious friends for company?' Robin replies. 'Even with the alcohol and the cold, that's rare, so let's assume something funny was going on. For now, at least.' He turns and faces the three in the ward again. 'Divide and conquer? Who do you want to go with?'

'Give me the bloke,' Freya says, pulling on her best smile. 'Let's see what this guy has to say.'

4

Sam Bowen is blond and blue-eyed, sitting up straight on the edge of his bed, fastening a flashy watch on his right wrist. His clothes suggest quality and expense: an Off-White logo on his shirt, a Barbour jacket on the chair next to him. He watches Robin as he goes over to his friend's bedside on the other side of the ward, then turns to Freya.

He switches on a smile: white teeth and false cheer.

'So, the male detective is interviewing the women, and you are talking to me,' he says. 'Is that how it works?' His accent is smooth, cut glass.

'How what works?' Freya asks.

'Do you find you get a better response if you interview the opposite gender?'

'Sometimes.'

'Interesting.' Another quick glance in the woman's direction, then back to Freya. 'How can I help you, Detective...'

'DC Freya West. I want to talk about last night.'

'Don't you need to warn me about my rights? That I can have a lawyer present?' He grins again. He reminds Freya of a wolf eyeing up his prey.

'I was getting to that.' She returns the smile. 'Would you like legal representation?'

'No. And I also can't tell you much that will help. I don't know what happened.'

'Start from the beginning. Why were you all there?'

'Friends getting together.'

'On a freezing cold beach?'

'Tradition.'

Freya pushes on, his short answers starting to grate. 'Friends from where?'

'How is this relevant?'

'Background.'

'Perhaps I do want that lawyer present after all.'

'You're not being accused of a crime, Mr Bowen.'

'Yet.' He crosses his arms over his chest, regarding Freya. Although his stance is confrontational, he seems to be amused, his lips curling up slightly at the edges. 'Do you mind?' he asks. 'Working on Christmas Day?'

'It's part of the job. I'm used to it.'

'But does it bother you?'

She sighs, annoyed at his persistence. 'No, not really.'

'Good to know.' He glances across at Robin again. 'Or maybe it's something else? Someone you want to get away from on Christmas Day, or someone you like being close to?'

'Neither.' Freya feels like he's being deliberately provocative. She chooses to ignore it. 'Just want to find out what happened to your friends. Where do you know each other from?' she asks again.

He shifts his gaze back to her. 'Does this normally work for you?'

'Does what normally work?'

'Your pretty blonde hair and innocent blue eyes? Do people trust you and tell you what you need to know?'

'People normally tell me what I need to know because they want to help solve a crime, Mr Bowen.'

'And you're sure that's what this is?' He waves away the question. 'Don't answer that. I'm leaving.' He stands up, picks up his jacket and drapes it over his arm. 'Nice to meet you, DC West.'

And with that, he walks away. Without even a second glance to his friends.

Freya watches him go. Just when you think you've met all the weird people in this world, someone like Sam Bowen comes along. She sighs, then turns her attention to Robin on the other side of the ward. Judging from his body language, it seems he's having just as much luck. His head is tilted towards the floor, brow furrowed. His notebook is still in his hand, but down at his side, as if he's given up on the idea of actually writing anything down. As she watches, the woman picks up her belongings and walks away.

Robin meets Freya's eyes, then heads across the ward to join her.

'Let me guess,' she says when he's by her side. 'Nothing?'

'An innocent catch-up between old friends,' he replies. 'Then she said she had to go and see her husband. And the other woman, Meg Carlton, upped and left while I was busy talking to Sara Williams.' He frowns. 'What are they playing at?'

They stand in silence. The festive sound of a Christmas carol drifts overhead, jarring in the sombre atmosphere of the ward.

'Do we need to inform any relatives?' Freya asks. 'About Alex's death?' She doesn't want to, but she'd rather go with Robin if needs must.

Robin shakes his head, to her relief. 'The only relative is an aunt in Birmingham. They'll send someone from West Mids to do it. No siblings, parents dead.'

Freya nods, glancing up at Robin, unable to avoid the comparison between her boss's family situation and the dead man's. But Robin's face remains impassive.

'What's next then, Sarge?' Freya asks, back to business. 'Shall we go after Meg Carlton?'

Robin thinks for a second, then shoves his notebook back into his bag. 'Not yet. My guess is she'll keep quiet, too.' He takes his hat out of his pocket and tugs it on with a grin. He's relishing the challenge, and she feels the same pull. Curiosity, mixed with determination to find out what these people are hiding.

'Let's head back to the station,' Robin says, decisively. 'The PCs on patrol are doing the house-to-house, looking for any other eyewitnesses. In the meantime, let's get some background on this lot. Because something funny is going on,' he continues. 'Something this group don't want us to know about.'

Freya nods, Robin echoing her own thoughts.

The response from these three, it's odd. People are usually glad to help, keen to do all they can to catch the fabled bad guy.

The innocent don't stonewall the police – unless they have something to hide.

5

'Meg, you shouldn't have left like that.'

Meg stands in the corridor in the hospital, glancing round nervously as Sara approaches. 'You could have at least tried to answer their bullshit questions,' Sara continues.

'Yes, but… I'm sorry, Sara, I panicked. Did you tell them anything?'

'Just that we were friends meeting up for drinks.'

Sara's annoyed. The last thing they need is Meg stressing. And she still can't get her head around the fact that Alex is dead. Out of nowhere, he's dead. Dead.

'But… what happened?' Meg stutters. 'Why did we all end up like that?'

'I don't know, Meg.'

'We hadn't drunk that much, had we? And Alex! How is Alex dead?'

'I said I don't know.' Sara snaps this time. Her head is thumping, the hangover making itself known. She shouldn't have drunk the vodka – and the rest. 'We don't know what happened. To us, or to Alex. Okay?'

'Okay,' Meg says quietly. 'But do you think it could be because… what Alex wanted to talk about?'

Sara glares at her. 'Meg, seriously. Shut the fuck up.'

Meg squeaks, but Sara ignores her as she spots Sam heading down the corridor towards them. His walk is confident, his posture straight. She knows Sam wouldn't have said anything stupid.

'I got your text,' he says to Meg when he's next to them. 'What do you want?'

'I...'

'Meg's stressing,' Sara interrupts.

'Oh, come on, Meggy. What are you worried about?'

'The police are involved, Sam!' she wails, and Sara rolls her eyes.

'We knew it was a possibility the police would speak to us at some point,' Sara snaps. 'So calm down, Meg, for Christ's sake.' She turns her attention to Sam. 'What the hell happened last night? Was that you?'

'Was what me?' he hisses back, his manner switching abruptly from casual cool to defensive. 'What are you asking? Did I drug all of us?'

'Yes! Mike has only just woken up, Sam! What did you do?'

Sam shakes his head, his eyes rising to the ceiling. 'Why do you assume it was me?'

'Because this would be just your thing. To mess with us all. And you haven't denied it.'

Sam lets out an exasperated sigh. 'No, I didn't drug us. Happy now? I have no idea what happened. Maybe Alex did it.'

'What was it?' Meg whispers.

'Who fucking knows,' Sam replies. 'Did you let them take your blood?'

Sara nods. They both look to Meg. She nods, too.

'I thought it would look bad if I said no,' she says. She starts crying and Sara thinks, shit, she hasn't changed. She was pathetic then, she's just as useless now.

'Well then, fine. I did, too, if you're wondering,' Sam adds. 'But it doesn't matter. We keep our mouths shut. Okay?' Sara nods, and they look to Meg again. She hesitates, but then nods quickly. 'About everything. What happened last night, included. Keep it vague. All of it.'

'Fine,' Sara replies. 'Now please can I go home? I need to talk to my kids.'

'And I need a long bath. I feel like I'll never be warm again,' Sam complains as he strides away.

Sara watches him go. She feels the same: despite the warming blankets in the ambulance, the hot tea, the change of clothes brought in by her mother. She feels the cold deep in her bones. It was freezing last night. She and Mike had sat in their car beforehand. She had seen the other vehicles: Sam's Audi, Meg's silly electric Leaf. Snow had been threatening, a few delicate flakes melting on the warm windscreen. She'd caught her husband's nervous glance.

'We could leave now,' she'd said, but Mike had one hand on the door already.

'No. Alex called us here. Let's find out what he has to say.'

And he'd opened the door and stepped out into the freezing cold. No hat, no gloves. Only his thin fleece for comfort. They hadn't intended to stay for long.

That was the last conversation they had. The two of them. Sara never needed much persuasion to have a drink or two, and even Mike joined in after his initial resistance. Alex's enthusiasm was always infectious, and who were they to say no to him now? Then the next thing she knew she was waking up on that beach, hard stones on her back, fingers and toes numb, whole body shaking. The fuggy confusion returns every time she tries to remember.

She wants to know. She wants the police to find out – that part at least. Because it scares her. Someone had tried to harm them. And, in the case of her husband and Alex, they'd succeeded.

6

Freya and Robin walk back to their cars, and Robin fills her in on what he'd found at the beach that morning.

'But why would you go on Christmas Eve,' Freya asks, 'in weather like that?' She remembers her own night in the pub: baking by the open fire, enjoying the company of other warm bodies, Josh pressed up tight against her. 'They weren't teenagers. They didn't need to be there.'

'Perhaps they wanted to celebrate in the open air,' Robin suggests, half-heartedly.

'But don't they have their own homes and gardens?' Freya says. Then she stops. 'What happened to your car?'

'Oh, that.' Robin bends down and prods at his bumper. Pieces of paint start to come away from the metal. 'Had a small altercation with a pole. I think it adds to the overall aesthetic.'

'In that it's a complete shit heap?'

'Hey, she can hear you,' Robin replies with a smile and an affectionate tap on the bonnet. 'I'll stick some tape on it later, it'll be fine. Meet me back at the nick? I'll get coffee.'

–

As Freya heads to the police station – slowly, she doesn't want her car to end up like Robin's – she realises she hasn't checked to see how Robin is. He *seems* okay, no more downcast than normal, but she knows Christmas must be impossibly hard for a man like him. He has nowhere to go, nobody to see. She knows he volunteers to be on call, saying he'd rather be the person working than someone with a family, and she's always been happy to be dragged along for the ride. But this year she has Josh. And that should have made things different.

She makes a quick call as she drives. It rings twice, then her mother answers, her voice clear over the loudspeaker.

'Freya? Hello, hello? Freya?'

'Yes, I can hear you, Mum. I'm sorry, I'm going to be a bit later than I planned.'

'It's fine, love. I'll move the timings. We'll eat this evening.' A voice calls from the background, her dad shouting. 'Yes, yes. I'll ask her. Is Josh still coming?'

Freya smiles. Her father has taken a shine to Josh, pleased to have some male company after years of Freya and her mother gossiping at the dinner table. 'Yes. Tell Dad he wants to talk about the Man United fixture on Boxing Day.'

The message is relayed to her father. 'They're going to be destroyed,' is shouted back.

She laughs. 'I'll call later with an update, Mum. Happy Christmas.'

'Happy Christmas, love.'

She pulls into the almost empty police station car park and turns off the engine. She's there before Robin and sends a quick text to Josh, updating him on what's going on. She looks at her watch – just past eleven. Maybe a few hours, and she could be in Salisbury, at her parents' house, by four? Salvage part of Christmas Day, at least.

In the main office, the majority of desks are quiet. Only a skeleton staff are in, the bare minimum to keep the place ticking over. She discards her coat and starts her computer up, wondering how much of this can wait until tomorrow. Then Alex Reynolds' face pops into her head. She remembers him from the case back in June. A man's body had been found in a dumped freezer; a case that eventually resulted in confessions from a few, a lengthy trial for the others. Unlike some duty solicitors, Freya had found Reynolds a pleasure to work with: someone who successfully walked the delicate line between caring for his clients and making sure justice was served. But she hadn't seen him for months, and now wonders what might have happened to him.

Robin emerges into the office, pulling the black beanie off his head. He shows no concern for his resulting hat hair, plastered down unattractively on his forehead. Two cardboard cups are held precariously in one hand.

'The best I could do,' he says, passing her one of the drinks. 'Stolen from Custody. Out of the machine. Everywhere's shut.'

Freya peers at it, dubiously. 'You could have just made one in the kitchen.'

'No milk.'

'But still.' She takes a tentative sip. It's okay.

'It's started snowing.' Robin brushes snowflakes from his coat then takes it off and drapes it over the back of his chair. 'Need to be careful we don't get stuck here.'

'God forbid,' she replies with a smile. 'Christmas with Robin Butler.' She takes a larger swig from her coffee and her body relaxes at the prospect of incoming caffeine. Then she jumps. 'Oh, shit, I forgot! This is for you.'

She digs into her bag and pulls out a small square box. She hadn't intended to get him anything but saw it and couldn't resist.

'You got me a present?' he says. He turns it over in his hand.

'Open it.'

'I—'

'I know, I know. You haven't got anything for me. It's only little. Don't worry.'

He frowns slightly, then pulls off the gold wrapping paper. He takes the mug out of its box. 'Mr Brave? Are you taking the piss?' he asks, a small smile on his face.

'No! But I saw it, and I thought of you. Because of everything you've been through, and how you are, and…' Her voice trails off in the face of his confused stare. 'Well,' she continues, feeling embarrassed. She points to the Little Miss Sunshine mug on his desk, with pigtails and freckles. 'It's a closer match than that one.'

'True.' He places it down and looks at it for a second. 'Thank you, Freya,' he adds quietly.

'No worries.'

He takes a sip from his coffee, staring at it. And with a jolt, Freya realises it might be the only Christmas present he's been given today. But what about Liam, his brother-in-law? Or Josie and Sandra and Finn, the closest people he has to family, living where he grew up in Devon? No, she reassures herself, there'll have been others.

But Robin has moved on, turning to his computer. 'So,' he begins. 'Since Intel are all out today, let's get some background done on this bunch, see where it takes us.' He picks up a pen and writes the five names on a pad next to him. 'Alex Reynolds, Mike and Sara Williams, Meg Carlton, Sam Bowen. How do they know each other?

What were they doing there last night? Jobs, families, friends.'

'And we'll need to follow up on CCTV,' Freya interjects. 'See what that shows us about last night. What buildings are nearby?'

'Possibly the sailing club? I'll see if there were any traffic or ANPR cameras on the A326.'

Freya turns to her computer and starts tapping. But as she does so, she hears someone arrive at the back of the office. A male voice, laughing in the corridor, then coming into the room. Freya feels her stomach lurch. Even after six months, she still sees Josh and thinks, *that's my boyfriend!* This attractive man, who's funny and charming and loved by everyone. That man is with *her*. He heads over, pulling his coat and bobble hat off, running his hand through his hair and quickly checking his reflection in the blackened screen of a computer.

Freya doesn't move, trying hard to remain cool. Next to her, Robin looks up, an unreadable expression on his face.

'What are you doing here?' she asks when he's next to her desk. She's beaming, she can't help it.

Josh smiles. 'No point sitting around your house by myself. So I thought I'd come in. Then we can at least be together on Christmas Day. Even if it's in this shithole.' He nods to Robin. 'Sarge,' he adds as a greeting.

'Nice of you to join us,' Robin replies. Freya gives him a quick look; he seems sincere. 'What are you working on?'

Josh dismisses the question. 'Cold case. Body found in a car park. We can't ID the vic and nobody's coming back to us because it's Christmas.' He shrugs. 'It can wait. Let me help with this one.'

Robin looks at him for a moment. Then he passes across a file. 'You can start on Sam Bowen.'

Josh takes it with a nod. Freya finds Josh's manner with Robin interesting. He treats Robin as the more senior and – let's face it – older copper that he is; he doesn't joke around with him in the same way he does with the other officers. But it's a savvy move on Josh's part. She knows Robin doesn't think much of him, and this seems to keep her boss's criticism at bay.

The three of them start work. After about ten minutes of tapping, Josh looks up.

'Can we put the radio on? A few Christmas songs to break up the silence?'

Freya glances at Robin. She knows he would rather eat his own arm than listen to what he describes as 'ear sewage', but to her surprise he nods.

Josh happily loads it up via his computer and sings along as they work. Freya starts with Sara and Mike Williams, consulting the usual sources of information – the Police National Computer, the Record Management System – before moving on to the good old internet and social media. Sara is a doctor, a GP at one of the local surgeries, her photo shown on their website. Freya looks through her public Instagram profile – she has two children, a girl and a boy, and a fondness for gin cocktails drunk in posh-looking wine bars. Her husband, Mike, is more discreet. All security settings are set to high for both Instagram and Facebook, but his own website is easy to find, advertising his services as a security consultant. She reads his bio, eyebrows rising with interest.

'Here,' she says. Robin looks over; Josh does the same. 'Mike Williams was a cop for fifteen years. Says he left in 2015.'

'Does it say what he did?'

'No. Do you think HR would give us his file?'

'Worth a try,' Robin agrees. 'What else do you have?'

Freya fills them in on what she's found out about Sara Williams, then Josh takes over, talking about Sam Bowen. A doctor with two PhDs in social psychology, he works as a therapist at his own practice, specialising in relationship counselling, trauma and grief.

'Clever bloke. What was he like when you met him?' Josh asks.

Freya thinks. 'Creepy,' she replies. 'Is he married?'

'Divorced. Twice.'

Freya raises her eyebrows. 'That's good going. Given he must be in his forties.'

'Forty-three,' Josh confirms. 'One child, a girl. Lives with her mum in the States by the looks of things. What about Meg Carlton?'

'Single, no children, as far as I can see,' Robin replies. 'No criminal record. She's a primary school teacher. Quiet life, not many friends. Just photos of her cat on Facebook. And a member of a few environmental groups.' Robin sits back in his seat, tapping his middle finger on the desk. 'One thing I did notice is that there aren't any photos of these guys on her social media. Not a single one.'

Freya swivels back and clicks on Sara's Instagram. She scrolls down the photos. 'Same here, and Sara Williams is a sociable bunny. Out with friends, drinking. Constantly.' She clicks through to Facebook, searching for the names, then sits back, confused. 'They're not even connected on Facebook.'

'So, what?' Josh asks. 'They're lying about knowing each other? Why else would they get together on Christmas Eve?'

Robin shrugs. 'Who knows. But we're not going to get much more out of this today. No one from HR is going to be in, even if we could persuade them to share Mike Williams' file. You two go, enjoy what's left of your day.'

Josh stands up almost instantly, but Freya hesitates. 'You're going to head off, too, right, Robin?' He hasn't moved from his desk. 'Right?'

Robin looks back to his computer. 'Yeah, sure,' he replies, although Freya's not convinced. 'I'll finish up here. Have a quick look into Alex Reynolds. Start on the CCTV.'

Freya feels Josh's eyes boring into the back of her head. 'Fine, okay. Merry Christmas, Sarge,' she says and feels Josh's hand take hers, pulling her out of the office.

But Robin doesn't reply. She looks back from the doorway; he's still sat at his desk, eyes focused on the screen.

7

Robin doesn't move as they leave, his eyes so fixed on the monitor they start to go dry. Then, once the door closes, he looks up.

He sighs. He still finds it hard to see Josh Smith as a nice guy. The two of them are so different. Where Josh is sociable, liked, life and soul of the Major Crimes unit, Robin is… not. Robin knows he's not an elegant man; he lumbers rather than strolls. He doesn't have Josh's easy charm, his good looks. And Robin finds it hard not to blame this bloke as the reason he doesn't see Freya as much as he used to.

In the past, before Freya met Josh, Robin had been Freya's default. Despite the fact they'd see each other every day at work, she'd drop round to his house in the evening. They'd have dinner together, watch TV. It had been nice to have her there. He'd enjoyed her company.

He's tried to fill the gap: see Liam more often, up the frequency of his running, even go on a few disastrous internet dates, but the fact remains, he misses her. Stupid, really. When she's here, in front of him, every day. But it's not the same. Taking the piss out of the procedural errors in *Line of Duty*. Debating who'll die next in *Game of Thrones*, both of them woefully behind.

He picks up the mug in front of him on the desk. He doesn't feel like Mr Brave. More like Mr Lonely. Mr Hanging-on-by-a-Thread. Especially on days like today.

And he has bought her a present. He opens his bottom desk drawer and pulls out the gift bag, removing the soft blue tissue paper and taking out the small box. He glances round, checking nobody is near, then opens it.

The pendant reflects in the overhead light. It's an intricate silver bee, on a delicate chain. He'd seen it while ambling around the shops, looking for something for Liam, and immediately bought it. Freya had been waffling on about bees all that week. She'd seen a documentary and been incensed: bees were extraordinary creatures, she'd passionately told him as they drove to a crime scene. And they were dying. Dying!

But now, looking at it, it seems wrong. It's too personal. More something a boyfriend should give, not a boss. He feels embarrassed that he's even bought it, and hurriedly puts it back in its bag and into the drawer. Fuck knows what he'll do with it now, but he can't give it to her. Absolutely not, no.

He turns his attention to his computer, trying to block thoughts of Freya and Christmas out of his mind. Alex Reynolds, he tells himself. He's what's important.

A man both he and Freya knew. A man who's dead.

So many questions need to be answered. Why are the other three being so evasive? Why were they there, on Christmas Eve, in below-zero temperatures? And how did they all end up unconscious – and Alex dead?

Robin's determined to find out. Christmas Day or not.

8

It's getting dark by the time Freya and Josh get close to their destination. The sun is setting, a slow dissolve of red and orange and yellow, tinting the sky as Salisbury Cathedral comes into view.

It's always the first glimpse of the cathedral that makes Freya feel like she's home. Even though there are miles to go on the journey, the sight of that tall gothic spire never ceases to create a warm glow inside. Josh is driving, Bombay Bicycle Club coming through on the speakers, bags of presents for her mum and dad on the back seat. Snow peppers the windscreen; she prays it won't worsen and hinder their progress. She's hungry, looking forward to the turkey, pigs in blankets, Yorkshire puddings.

'Yes, Yorkshire puddings,' she'd said to a disbelieving Josh. 'Why not?'

'Because they're not Christmassy,' he replied.

'But they're the best part of a roast, and Christmas is all about the best parts of everything.'

He accepted that explanation, checking first that they weren't replacing something essential. Like roast potatoes or stuffing or cauliflower cheese.

'No, it'll all be there,' she replied.

She's slightly nervous now, thinking about the Wests' Christmas traditions Josh is going to be exposed to. Things she has come to see as normal – like the stocking she still has, at the age of thirty-seven, under the tree – that he might find silly.

'What if my mum gets drunk and flirts with you?' she says now, the latest in a long line of worries she's voiced.

'Then I'll flirt back,' he replies, throwing her a big grin. 'Freya, stop fretting. It's going to be fun.' He reaches across and grabs her hand, giving it a quick squeeze.

'Josh?'

'Hmm?'

She's feeling bad for leaving Robin alone at the station. She knows he has nowhere else to be.

'Do you think I should have invited Robin?'

'Invited Robin where?' He takes his eyes off the road for a second. 'You don't mean today? No, Freya.' He shakes his head emphatically. 'You don't invite your superior officer along for Christmas dinner at your parents' house. That's weird.'

'But he's not just my sergeant. He's my...'

Josh gives her a strange look. 'He's your what?'

She turns and looks out of the window. 'No, you're right,' she says quietly. 'It would be weird.'

She directs Josh round the ring road, skirting the outside of the city. Junctions and roundabouts where she learned to drive, where she stalled, beeped and cursed to pass her test on the fifth attempt. Past the Grasmere House Hotel, where her new employer had discovered she was no good at silver service and plonked her behind the bar as soon as she turned eighteen. And all the while, she's thinking about Robin, and the answer to that question.

She was going to say, *friend*. He's my friend. But their relationship goes way beyond that. They know secrets about each other that could destroy their lives; the events of last October cemented their bond in a way that Josh could never understand. So, no, friend doesn't feel right.

She remembers Sam Bowen's bizarre observation in the hospital. *Someone you want to get away from on Christmas Day, or someone you like being close to?* A perception from a stranger, but so close to the truth she finds it uneasy. She never minds being on call with Robin; she looks forward to seeing his number on her screen, knowing it's the start of a case. Some noteworthy like this one, others thought-provoking. But whatever they end up with, she enjoys working with Robin, bouncing ideas off one another, their partnership balanced despite their unequal ranks.

'Where here?' Josh asks, interrupting her chain of thought before it reaches a conclusion.

'Left. Follow signs to Barford.'

The conversation about Robin has dulled their good cheer. Freya lost in her worry; Josh confused by the strange about-turn in her mood.

This is new territory for Josh. He's met her parents a few times, but on home turf, when they drove up to her house in Winchester. This is the first time he's been here. She hasn't met his parents, although she knows he speaks to them on the phone every week. Work schedules haven't been compatible with a trip to Newcastle.

But now, here they are. Josh does a perfect parallel park outside the small semi. She sees it with fresh eyes – shabby and neglected. Paint peeling from the brickwork, trees and shrubs in the small front garden cut back harshly for the winter. Moss growing on the porch.

She gets out of the car, grabs the presents and opens the squeaking gate. Josh takes her hand, their overnight bags thrown over his shoulder.

'I bet this garden is gorgeous in the summer,' he says.

She grins. 'It is,' she replies. 'My mum's pride and joy.'

They walk up the narrow path, but the door's open even before they're halfway there. Freya's mum beams. She's wearing a silver sparkly shirt, a long velvet skirt and flashing Christmas tree earrings. She has a red apron over the top. Like Freya, she's tall and slim, her blonde hair now faded to grey-silver.

Freya can't help but smile, all worries vanished. She squeezes Josh's hand. It's right that they're here. Just the two of them. She's quickly enveloped in her mother's hug, as delicious smells drift from the open doorway.

'And here's Josh!' her mum says. 'I'm so pleased you two made it. When you phoned and said you'd been called in, I feared the worst.'

'There's no way I was missing out on your roast, Mrs West,' Josh says. 'I'd have come by myself if need be.'

'And you would have been more than welcome. Come in, come in.'

A small brown-and-white dog dashes towards them, barking. Barnaby, her parents' Cavalier King Charles Spaniel, is every bit the entitled royal hound. He stops when he sees Josh, and growls.

'Ah, Barnaby, enough of that,' Freya's father says from the doorway. A few inches taller than Josh's six foot, he cuts an impressive figure, the demeanour from his former career in business a hard habit to break. He gives Josh a hearty clap on the back.

'Good to see you again, lad,' he says. 'Now,' he addresses Freya, after they've finished their hug. 'Tell me about this case. None of your confidentiality rubbish either.'

'No, no. No dead bodies over dinner,' Freya's mum scolds.

'How long until dinner?'

'Fifteen minutes.'

Her father shows Freya and Josh into the living room with a wink. Although Freya's career choice drastically differed from his own, he'd always been a hundred per cent behind her decision to join the force. An attitude now reinforced by his fascination with her cases. 'Quarter of an hour then,' he says. 'Start talking.'

Freya settles on the sofa with a glass of champagne; Josh opts for red wine and installs himself next to her.

She gives a quick summary, her dad listening closely. Five friends celebrating Christmas on a beach. One dead, one in hospital. Three not talking.

'What's your working theory?' he asks. 'Somebody did something nasty and they're all covering?'

'We don't even know if it is a suspicious death yet,' Freya replies. She takes a sip from her glass: it is exactly what she needs, crisp and fruity on her tongue. 'Waiting on the blood tests and the PM.'

'So, are they victims or suspects?'

'At the moment, both.'

'Maybe it's perfectly innocent,' Josh suggests. 'The deceased was a lawyer, one of them used to be a cop. Perhaps that makes them overly cautious.'

'Seems a bizarre way to avoid suspicion,' her father answers. 'Refusing to talk.' He points a finger at Freya. 'Puts the onus on you. To find something to incriminate them.' Her father leans back in his chair. 'You should be running this. Not playing second fiddle to your sergeant. When are you going to apply for promotion?'

'It's not like that,' Freya replies. 'And when I'm ready.'

'You're ready now. How long have you been a DC? Five years?'

'Nearly seven,' she says meekly. She catches Josh's look, echoing her father's disapproval. 'You can't talk,' she directs to him. 'You used to be a DS in Newcastle. You've done the exams. Why aren't you looking for something?'

'Who says I'm not?' Josh counters.

They're interrupted by a call from the kitchen. 'Dinner,' her mother shouts. 'Come to the table.'

–

Freya can't possibly eat any more. Her plate is clear, but the food is far from finished.

'Mrs West—'

'Cathy. Please, Josh.'

'You have outdone yourself. This was delicious.'

Her mother beams with pride and starts to collect their plates.

'No, no, we'll do it,' Josh says. 'Please. You put your feet up.'

Freya hauls herself out of her chair, then follows Josh as they clear the table. She puts a few plates in the dishwasher before Josh moves her aside.

'Please, no,' he says. 'I've seen how you load yours and I can't bear it. A meal like this needs precision. Expertise.'

'There's no way you'll get all this in.'

'Stand aside, amateur.'

She laughs and lets him take over. It might be the champagne talking – and the wine with dinner, and the sugar rush from the Christmas pudding – but Josh being here has been perfect. It's made it better: her father enjoying the football talk, her mother basking in his compliments.

She hears a call from the living room.

'Presents!' her father shouts. 'Washing-up comes later. It's time for presents!'

9

Although Robin has always been happy in his own company, Christmas definitely makes it harder.

He's made some progress. The SOCOs have found Reynolds' keys and he's been promised them in the morning. Same with the phone: when Greg finally hauls his lazy butt out of bed, it will be the first thing the Digital team look at.

ANPR and traffic cameras have come up empty, although he's had more luck with the CCTV. A security camera on the side of the sailing club catches part of the car park; the owner's sending it over tomorrow.

Reynolds was single, no kids. He had no family except for an aunt, now notified of his death. Robin spoke to her on the phone: she was upset but composed, and said she'd be happy to talk when she comes down from Birmingham to identify the body tomorrow. Robin wants a full picture of the man he was.

Robin only has a snippet so far. Alex worked hard, travelled extensively in his time off. He went out occasionally, to the pub – although, as they'd already observed, not in the company of any of the other four. But Robin had also noticed one other thing: Alex's posts were less frequent recently. More comments on Twitter about television programmes and Netflix, fewer photos from far-flung locations. His world seems to have narrowed.

But he hits a dead end. It's Christmas Day, nobody is at work. Nobody to respond to his requests for information. He picks up his bag, carefully places his new mug inside, and goes home.

The roads are quiet as he drives. The snow has abated but it's still below zero, the wind cutting and harsh. Robin imagines warmth and laughter behind the closed doors of the houses he passes; loved ones all together, board games, the *Strictly* special.

He remembers his family Christmases as a child. He and his older sister Georgia waking early, comparing the weight of the stockings at the foot of their beds. Being told by their parents to go away: 'it's four in the morning'. They'd both go into Georgia's room, sit under her duvet, excitedly talking about what presents might be waiting for them under the tree and eating the majority of the Cadbury selection box, until even Robin felt sick. Later, after his mother died, dinner was spent either with Josie and her son Finn – Robin's childhood best friend – or with Sandra, their other neighbour. All of them crammed around the Butlers' small dining table. Tiny, terraced houses next door to each other, paper-thin walls, and the people Robin had grown up with. Those were the best. Robin's favourite Christmases. The noise, conversations merging, bursting across one another; laughter as trinkets flew across the room from pulled crackers.

As a cop, he knows that isn't the reality for everyone. Expectations are high; money worries create arguments. Too much drinking, relatives who haven't seen each other in years forced together in cramped houses. Incidents of domestic violence escalate; the teams on Response will be busy tonight. It's little comfort.

He is alone. His parents are both dead. His sister and his nephews, too, killed in a hit-and-run over six years ago. Both Sandra and Josie had invited him down for Christmas, but Devon is too far and he's on call. He hasn't been to visit as much as he'd have liked. He thinks about Finn, now moved back in with his mum as his rehabilitation continues, following the terrible events of last June when he was arrested for murder. Soon, Robin thinks. Soon he'll make time to see them.

He gets home, takes his coat off, hangs it up. Shoes kicked into the cupboard under the stairs. He walks through to his kitchen and opens the fridge, staring into it solemnly. He should have thought this through, planned something nice to eat at least. He takes out a beer, closes the fridge, then moves on to the freezer. Pizza it is then.

He turns on the oven and shoves it in, then picks up his bag and empties it on the table. Investigation notebook for Alex Reynolds, a few printouts from the internet thrown in to read tonight. And the mug from Freya.

He thinks about her, wondering what she's doing right now. He knows she's gone back home, Josh in tow.

Unusually for Freya – who normally shares everything on her mind the minute it enters her head – she's been surprisingly tight-lipped about Josh. Maybe she's detected the air of slight animosity; maybe she doesn't want to rub in her newly coupled-up status when he is so resolutely single. He doesn't know, but he is aware of the amount of time Freya and Josh spend together. He's noticed the slight touch of their hands when they go to lunch, the way she watches him across the incident room, a small smile on her face.

DCI Baker was indifferent when she told him. Robin was secretly hoping for a little more resistance.

'I don't give a shit,' Baker had confided to Robin after. 'Just make sure they keep it professional around the nick.'

And they had. You could barely tell, had it not been for their colleague, Mina, and her unsubtle innuendos, and the slight flush of Freya's cheeks when she's around him.

The buzzer rings, announcing his pizza. He puts his new mug next to the kettle, then grabs his meal out of the oven.

Half an hour later, he's full of carbs and cheese and processed meat. He burps loudly. One of those *Mission Impossible* films is showing so he watches it, convinced he's seen it before. And the ache in the pit of his stomach grows.

He misses his sister. The year before she died, they had Christmas at her house, his two year-old nephews hysterically excited about everything. Their present from Robin – a massive plastic garage – received enthusiastic squeals and he sat on the floor next to them, zooming cars down the ramps and up the lift, accompanied by constant chatter and ear-numbing electronic beeps. That was the last time he was truly happy, he thinks. Surrounded by the people he loved, that loved him. A too familiar wave of sadness threatens. He wants to go to bed, pull the duvet over his head and stay there until the world disappears. Either that or drink until his mind is numb.

But he's been there before. And he resolved to never go that far again. His default position, isolation, does him no favours. There are people, he tells himself sternly, who care about him. Freya, with her silly gifts and constant chatter. Liam, his brother-in-law: solid, giver of strong bear hugs. And the closest thing to family he has, down in Devon.

He picks up the phone and dials a number.

'Hi, Josie,' he says when she answers. 'How are you?'

And the evening gets that little bit better.

10

Freya lies awake in the darkness of her old bedroom. The walls have been repainted, the furniture changed, but the shadows on the ceiling, the way the light falls against the walls, that's the same. She can hear her father moving about downstairs in the kitchen; she can vividly imagine him as he dries up, folding the tea towel into four perfect quarters and hanging it on the rail. The little habits, the smells, the family jokes – it's all here. Freya feels like she's a vessel, topped up with love.

Next to her, Josh shifts slightly in his sleep. His body is warm, and she snuggles next to him, resting the palm of her hand gently on the soft cotton of his T-shirt. A concession to being under her parents' roof when he normally sleeps in just his boxers.

Freya knows he feels odd, being in the same room together.

'My parents aren't naive,' Freya had told him. 'They know we're not saving ourselves for marriage.'

'I know. But still.'

'Don't worry, I'm not going to force you into loud sex.'

He'd smiled. 'Fine,' he'd said, then shaken his head. 'I never thought the day would come when I would be pleased about not having a shag.'

But now she's here, pleasantly pissed, she realises that actually, she would like that, very much.

She pushes up against him, running her hand under his T-shirt. He stirs as she continues her quest, sleepily returning her kiss. She can see him in the dark, his eyes half-open, but interested.

'You said we wouldn't,' he whispers.

She gently pulls her top over her head, then pushes his T-shirt up, skin against skin.

'We can be quiet,' she says.

'Very quiet.'

'Like mice.'

'Tiny shagging mice.'

Then his mouth is on hers. Hands, exploring. A stifled groan from him, a shush from her. Giggling. Frantic scrabbling in the dark for a condom. He moves on top of her, slowly, both aware of every creak of the bed, every noise that might give them away.

–

After, Josh falls asleep almost instantly, but she lies awake, his arm around her, her head resting on his chest. These last six months with Josh have been perfect. Day by day she's changed her initial perception of him: he's not the player she thought he was. He flirts, yes, but with everyone: a natural charm attracting attention wherever he goes.

He's different to the men she'd been used to.

In the darkness, she lets herself remember Jonathan. He was quieter, more self-contained. He took up less space in the world than Josh demands.

For her birthday, the only one she'd had the chance to spend with Jonathan, he'd taken her to the beach. With a kite. In December. He'd remembered a throwaway comment – that it was something she liked to do with her dad when she was a child – and they'd spent the day laughing and joking, cheeks freezing in the wind while they ate fish and chips on the sea wall.

This year, Josh had taken her to a fancy restaurant. Lavish attention, posh champagne, gorgeous food. Josh had seemed right at home. He'd joked with the waiters, ordering in perfect French, looking bloody amazing in his suit and tie. But she hadn't *relaxed*. Not knowing what to wear, unfamiliar high heels, too many items on the menu she couldn't pronounce, let alone be brave enough to order. But she'd enjoyed it, of course she had. And why wouldn't she?

She lifts her head and kisses him lightly on the cheek, her lips grazing his dark stubble. When she'd seen him arrive at the office that afternoon, her heart had made a little leap. He was there, for her. He is here, for her.

This gorgeous, lovely man. He is hers.

And with that last thought, she falls asleep.

11

Sunday

It's ten a.m., they're standing in the road outside Alex Reynolds' house, and Freya stifles a yawn. She'd dragged Josh out of bed first thing, him protesting strongly at the loss of her mother's fried breakfast.

'Can't Butler go by himself?' Josh had asked, cradling a mug of strong coffee as Barnaby licked his bare feet under the kitchen table.

'No. And I owe it to Alex.'

Josh had shaken the dog away from his toes. 'Point taken,' he'd said gravely.

Josh knew Alex, too, and his death had surprised him as much as it had Freya. Now, standing, freezing, by his front door, she feels curiosity, as much as sadness, to know why this guy's life ended so prematurely.

Robin puts the key in the lock and they step over the threshold. They're wearing the usual gloves and shoe covers; it's dark inside and Robin flicks on the light. The hallway is tidy but sparse: a line of men's shoes by the front door, three coats hanging up on the hooks above. A staircase in front of them, a door to the side. The stillness is eerie, a house in mourning. They go through.

Christmas cards line the mantelpiece. A small gawdy fake tree glistens by the window. The sofas are brown leather, the television huge, surrounded by an impressive sound system. A pile of magazines and papers lie on the side table, next to a pair of glasses and a few biros. A bookcase with some paperbacks, photos in frames, piles of CDs and DVDs at the bottom.

'Here, look,' Robin says. He holds out a photo. It looks old: a man and a woman standing with their arms around each other, impressive scenery behind. 'His parents,' he says. 'Died when he was seventeen.'

'Both?' Freya asks. 'And so young.'

'Car accident,' he replies. 'He lived with his aunt until he went to uni.' She glances across, knowing the similarity to Robin's own life. 'She'll be here just before lunch,' he adds, then turns before she can catch his expression, putting the photo down and walking through to the kitchen.

Freya stays next to the bookcase. A few ornaments decorate the shelves: a large glass paperweight with *Most Promising Graduate* engraved on it, a company logo below of an entwined C and R. A small pot, filled with pebbles and shells. Freya tips a few out into her hand, then puts them back. There's nothing helpful here.

'How was your evening?' she shouts to Robin in the kitchen.

'Quiet,' he calls back. 'Worked.'

She pauses, waiting to be asked the same question but he's silent.

'I'm going to the bedroom,' she replies and receives a non-committal grunt in response, so she doubles back and walks up the stairs. The photos on the wall as she heads up show gorgeous panoramic views of mountains and beaches. Some include groups of people, Alex among them. In others he's alone. None of them include the four he was with when he died.

She walks into his bedroom. The bed is made, the sheets plain. The bedside table is empty, except for a book left open, marking the spot, spine broken. A story he'll never finish.

She opens the wardrobe – suits and shirts and ties, the dress of a criminal lawyer, although not one with much money, she thinks, as she checks the labels. Next, M&S. A smarter one in dark grey from Hugo Boss: weddings and funerals or the cases that count, she assumes. She shuts it and turns her attention to the chest of drawers.

Same here: boxers, socks, T-shirts. Nothing interesting. Until she gets to the bottom drawer. Personal items: souvenirs and keepsakes, maybe. An old bath toy in the shape of a large frog, plastic cracking and aged. A tiny Cub Scout uniform, badges sewn onto the sleeve. And a shoebox. She pulls it out and rests it on the bed, then crouches on her knees in front of it. The box is dusty, but there are fingermarks across the top, as if someone had been looking in it recently. She opens the lid.

Inside are photos. Mostly six-by-four, all fairly old. A few passport prints of a young Alex, and then shots of him with various people. They all look late teens, maybe early twenties: fuzzy selfies taken the old-fashioned way, by holding a clunky camera out in front of you, hoping the lens was pointing in the right direction. Men smiling – Alex included, with a big grin – pints of beer on the table, arms round each other. Women laughing, dancing in a dingy-looking club. Tired students sitting in a grubby house on an old sofa, posters of Nirvana and *The Crow* tacked up messily on the wall.

'Robin!' Freya shouts. She doesn't look away from the box, fingers flicking through the pile of photographs.

'What?' Robin appears in the doorway. 'Have you got something?'

Freya looks up. 'This is it,' she says, holding out the photos. 'Look – it's them.' She points and he takes a few. 'Alex, Sara, Mike, Meg and Sam. The age of the photographs, the surroundings, the pubs,' she gabbles. 'This is how they know each other. They were at university together.'

12

'Wow, I mean… you're right.' Robin kneels next to Freya on the carpet and starts looking through the photographs. Some of the shots are blurry, out of focus. They all look like kids: hair longer, eyes bright, cheeks full, clothes shabby. But they are unmistakably the same people.

'And here?' Freya says. She points to a shot: a group of them sitting on a sofa, foam sprouting out of one of the arms, covered in what looks like two sleeping bags. Robin turns the photo over. *When the heating broke down* is scrawled on the back. 'I think they lived together,' Freya finishes.

'Any idea where?'

'That's just it! I recognise the pub. See?' Freya holds up a different photo. Alex and Sara, pints of beer in their hands in a concrete pub garden. 'This is The Hobbit. And this one – this is the Dog and Duck. They must have gone to university here, same as me.'

'I know The Hobbit,' Robin comments. 'In Portswood. So they didn't go far.'

'Obviously not.' She looks back to the pile, grabbing a handful and flicking through them. 'And here, look. Do you think this was their house?'

Robin takes the photo. It's faded, slightly out of focus, but he recognises them all. They're standing outside a terraced house, paint peeling on the windowsill, weeds sprouting proudly through the concrete, a full wheelie bin in shot. He traces their faces along the line, then turns it over. In biro, written on the back: *The Five.*

'Can we check the council tax records for that time?' Freya says, thinking out loud. 'Track down the address. One of them must have registered.'

'We'll get Intel on it,' Robin confirms.

Freya sits back on her knees. 'Did you find anything downstairs?'

'No, nothing out of the ordinary for a forty-something bloke.' And it occurs to him for the first time: they are the same age. Him and Alex Reynolds. It makes him feel odd, that in a different world this might have been his house. His death. He takes a deep breath then points across the landing. 'Have you checked the bathroom?'

'Not yet.'

He replaces the photos, then stands, stretching and walking into the bathroom. It's clean and tidy, a few toiletries on the side of the bath, but otherwise bare. He opens the cupboard – towels, toilet roll, but… this is unusual. Drugs, and lots of them. Boxes of pills, and not the common over-the-counter sort either. He takes a few out: diazepam, cyclizine, domperidone, oxycodone, gabapentin. A box of something called buprenorphine patches, and a small brown bottle of oramorph. He checks the labels: all prescribed to Alex Reynolds. And all over the last six months.

He pulls his phone out of his pocket and makes a call. A weary voice answers on the third ring.

'Steph, if I read you a list of drugs, can you tell me what they might be used for?'

A sigh greets him. 'Hello to you, too, Butler. Go on then.'

He reads the names.

'Well,' Steph begins. 'Diazepam is a benzodiazepine, commonly prescribed for decreasing anxiety or muscle spasms. Gabapentin is a neuropathic pain medication. Cyclizine and domperidone are anti-emetics. Stop you puking. And oxy, I'm sure you know about.'

'Pain relief?'

'Right. Same as the oramorph and buprenorphine. But all of these in combination are often used in the palliative care of end-stage cancer.' Another pause. 'Who is this for, Robin?'

'Alex Reynolds. The guy from the beach yesterday.'

'Oh, okay. Interesting. I'm waiting on his medical records but I'll get to the PM this afternoon.'

'I'll be there. Thanks, Steph.'

Robin hangs up, then takes photographs of the drugs. Freya appears at his side. He points to the array of pharmaceuticals in the cabinet and Freya gives a low whistle.

'Steph says they're all for end-stage cancer.'

'Seriously?' Freya's eyes are big and blue with surprise. 'Poor bloke.'

For the first time Robin considers whether Alex Reynolds' demise was deliberate. Wrenching the control away from the tumours, choosing death on his own terms. Maybe the others weren't talking for good reason: assisting suicide is a crime, punishable by imprisonment, if convicted.

'We'll know more after Steph's done the PM,' Robin says. 'Later today.'

'Oh, okay.' She pauses and he waits, knowing she has something to ask him. 'Do you mind going alone?' she says at last. 'I'll be there for the interview with the aunt.

It's just… Josh wants to go to West Quay, and I promised I'd go with him.'

He tilts his head to one side. 'Captain America wants to go shopping?'

'Yes, okay?' she replies, clearly bristling. 'Some men care about how they look, Butler.'

'I don't know what you mean. I care.'

'Sure.' She looks him up and down, pointedly. He's wearing jeans, a pair of old Adidas Gazelle trainers and a grey hoodie with the line-up from Reading Festival 1997 on the back.

'It's vintage,' he replies.

'Vintage doesn't just mean old, Robin.' And with a slight pull at his sleeve, she walks away, chuckling.

He stares after her. What on earth does she mean? he wonders. There's nothing wrong with his jumper. Then he follows her down to fetch the evidence bags.

13

Alex Reynolds' aunt looks like him, Robin observes. Something about the eyes, the long, narrow nose. She's angular, like he was, and lean.

'We're sorry for your loss,' Robin begins. 'Thank you for coming.'

They're sitting on sofas in the family room of the police station. She arrived bang on one o'clock, as she said she would; everything about her indicates precision. Blue jeans, white shirt, navy jumper. All crisp and ironed. A small, neat handbag, from which she now takes a pocket-sized packet of tissues.

'Of course.' She sniffs, dabbing at her nose, then takes a sip from her plastic cup of water. 'Anything for Alex.'

'When was the last time you saw him?'

'About a month ago. You know about the cancer?' Freya nods. 'He wasn't able to drive anymore so I came down to see him.' She's the sister of Alex's father, and his only surviving relative. She speaks with a broad Black Country accent. 'Took him out for dinner, although his appetite wasn't up to much. Broke my heart, I can tell you, to see him that way.'

'What was Alex like?'

She sits up straight on the sofa. Her eyes are red-rimmed and puffy, but she's composed and attentive. 'Full of life and energy,' she begins. 'Even when he got ill, it didn't seem to slow him down, at first. That's why it was such a shock when the policeman came. I thought he'd have months left.' She smiles, sadly. 'Can you tell me more about how he died? The policeman was vague.'

Robin frowns. 'We don't know much, at this point. Alex was found on Calshot beach on Christmas morning. He'd spent the night there with some friends. We'll know more when our pathologist has had a chance to examine him.'

'And you'll update me?'

'Of course.'

Next to him, Freya pulls a photo from the evidence bag – the one of 'The Five' outside the house – and hands it to Robin. 'Do you recognise any of these people, Ms Reynolds?' he asks.

She digs in her handbag for a small pair of reading glasses and puts them on. She leans forward and squints at the photo.

'These were the people he was with?' she asks, looking up for a moment then peering at it again. Robin nods. 'I met them, but only a few times, when Alex was at university. He lived with them. What were they doing at the beach?' A puzzled look comes over her face. 'Out in the elements? It must have been freezing.'

'We're not sure yet. Had Alex talked about these friends since university?'

'No. And that surprised me. Whenever Alex phoned during that time, he would go on and on about what they'd been up to. Mike, yes? And one of the girls was called Sally or Sasha?'

'Sara,' Robin confirms.

'Yes. That's it. But once he left uni, he didn't mention them at all. When I asked, he was evasive. Said he didn't speak to them anymore. But he was there with them on Christmas Eve? Can't they say what happened?'

'They were unconscious, too,' Robin says.

'Oh.' She picks up the photo and looks at it again. Then she jolts, as a thought occurs to her. 'You think someone deliberately harmed Alex and his friends?'

'I'm afraid we just don't know at this stage. But yes, we're not ruling anything out.'

'Why would someone want to hurt Alex?'

'Did he ever mention anyone he had problems with?'

'No, never.'

Her attention drops to the photo again, her hand over her mouth, deep in thought.

Robin looks over at Freya. She's been watching the conversation so far, a sympathetic expression on her face. Now she sits forward, ready to speak.

'Ms Reynolds,' she says. 'When you last saw him, was Alex depressed?'

'Depressed?' Ms Reynolds looks up again, giving the question some thought. Robin likes her. The way she considers her answers, rather than just blurting out the first thing that comes into her head. It makes his job easier. A witness account he can trust.

'He was sad,' she continues. 'But you'd expect that from someone with his diagnosis. The doctors originally gave him six months to live. They didn't put it like that, though. Said, you know, 90 per cent of patients with your progression of the illness... blah blah.' She sighs, annoyed. 'Basically, they were giving him six months. But Alex never let that affect him. He said he'd take every minute he could get.'

Robin feels Freya glance his way. The aunt catches the expression.

'No,' she says, with defiance.

'Ms Reynolds?' Robin asks.

'No, he didn't kill himself, if that's what you're asking. There's no way.' Robin notices her eyes flare with anger and he steels himself before asking the next question.

'How can you be sure?' he replies, gently.

She shakes her head quickly, her body language tense. 'No. Not Alex. His parents died when he was seventeen. In a car accident.'

She looks to Freya for a response. 'We're aware, yes,' Freya replies.

'And when his parents died, he was distraught, as any other teenage boy would be. But he was also determined. He said he would live every day for them. And he did. That boy had more lust for life than anyone I've ever met. Places he wanted to travel to, cultures he wanted to experience. He devoted his whole career to defending people in trouble, to helping others and doing his parents proud. So no, Alex didn't kill himself.' She leans forward on the sofa, punching the air with a finger in their direction. 'Don't you dare take the easy way out, Detectives. You investigate Alex's death as fully as you can, until you find who did this to him.' She looks Robin right in the eye. 'Promise me?'

Robin nods, solemnly. 'We will.'

–

She leaves, and Robin and Freya watch her go. Robin knows she has the hard part next: identifying her nephew's body. His heart goes out to her; he's been there himself. Not for his nephews, that had fallen to Liam. But his sister, six years ago. Liam refused, saying he didn't want to remember Georgia that way. Nor had Robin, but the job had to be done.

He's had new-found admiration for the pathology team since that day. Despite the violent nature of her death – the glass from the windscreen that cut her face, the broken bones and bruises – she looked almost peaceful. Her wounds had been mended as best they could; her hair had been washed of blood, her eyes closed. They treated him with respect and care, giving him space when he needed it, the support after.

He hopes never to have to go through that again.

Freya turns to him now.

'What do you make of that?' she asks. 'Her assertion that Alex didn't kill himself?'

He nods, sadly, and they both start back to the office.

'We do as we said,' he replies as they walk. 'We keep digging.'

14

The pain comes in waves. Sharp, biting, teeth-clenching pain, as his damaged nerve endings come back to life.

Mike is at the mercy of the doctors and nurses. Nameless people drift in and out of his consciousness, administering drugs, rebandaging his fingers. As they warm his hands in the water baths, the cloying smell of antiseptic in the air, he studies the mess. Blackened tips, giving way to angry red flesh. Swollen, tight blisters. White flaky skin.

Anything to distract him from the burning agony before the medication kicks in.

He hates feeling this helpless. He has nowhere to funnel the anger, the fury he feels towards whoever instigated this tragedy. Whoever killed Alex.

When Sara told him the news, his mind felt as broken as his weak frozen body. Seeing Alex again had been exactly the balm he needed. Alex's big, wicked smile, brandishing that bottle of Famous Grouse. The stuff they had drunk at uni: the two of them, giggling like schoolboys on the sofa, watching *Trainspotting* or *Reservoir Dogs* for the thousandth time on VHS, before going out to the pub.

The sight of him broke his heart at first. Narrow wrists. Cracked, bitten lips. And thin, too thin. Alex shifted position carefully, like every movement brought him pain. But underneath the sunken cheekbones, he was still the same old Alex. His pragmatism and determination. He always knew the best course of action – back then, whether it was which club to go to or which woman to snog.

'Everything will be okay, Mikey,' he said on Christmas Eve. 'We do the right thing, and our consciences will be clear.'

But someone disagreed.

And now Alex is dead.

The nurse arrives and dispenses a fresh flood of relief. Mike lies back and closes his eyes as the numbness washes over him. And one thought comes into his head, before his mind drifts into oblivion.

Alex was wrong. Everything will not be okay. And Mike is still as scared as he always was, all those years ago.

15

Freya is loving everything about this. From the feeling of Josh's warm hand in hers, to giving her opinions in the changing room in Jack Wills – she feels like his girlfriend. His proper actual *girlfriend*.

The shopping centre is busy, Christmas sales in full flow. Kids dash past them, harried parents in their wake. Pushchairs bump against her ankles, large men jostle her with bags of shopping, but she doesn't care one bit.

'That would look good on you,' Josh says, pointing to the dress she's been holding for five minutes. 'Try it on.'

'It's too low-cut.'

'It absolutely is not,' Josh laughs. 'No such thing.'

Reluctantly, she trails to the changing room; he follows behind, passing her another two tops as she goes. This aspect of him, it's surprising. She knows he's more interested in fashion than your average bloke, but he can also tell instinctively what will suit her.

She tries the dress on. She's surprised to see how much it flatters her boobs, highlights her waist.

'Let me see?' comes the voice from outside.

She opens the curtain and stands in front of him, feeling slightly abashed. 'See!' Josh says triumphantly. 'I was right!' He turns to the saleslady, who's been watching. 'Wasn't I?'

She nods with an indulgent smile. 'Fine,' Freya replies. 'I'll get it.'

She goes back inside with a swoosh of the curtain. How can things be going this well? she thinks as she gets dressed. How?

Outside the shop, Josh pulls her to face him, and puts his arms round her shoulders. 'Are you hungry?' he asks with a smile.

'Starving.'

He kisses her lightly, and they start walking towards the lifts to the food court. 'What do you fancy? Burgers? Wagamama?'

'Joshua?'

The voice comes from behind them. Freya feels Josh tense.

'I knew it was you! Joshua, how funny bumping into you here.'

They turn to face a woman: tall, impossibly slim, with long brown hair styled into precise curls. Her dark eyes don't shift from Josh; she doesn't acknowledge Freya.

'Elise,' Josh says, his voice slow. 'How are you?'

Josh's arm feels heavy round Freya's shoulders. She instantly feels on edge. It's Elise, of course it is. The ex-girlfriend he moved down from Newcastle to be with. Who dumped him within a month of his arrival.

Who looks like a fucking fashion model.

'I'm good! I'm good! And who is this?'

She turns her attention to Freya for the first time, looking at her like she's a ten-year-old.

'Freya.' Josh glances down and meets her gaze for a second. 'Freya, this is Elise.'

'Nice to meet you.' Freya forces a smile and holds out her hand. Elise shakes it, her fingers limp.

'Aren't you lovely?' Elise says. 'This is Franco.' The man next to her – dark, movie-star handsome, a beard so styled it looks glued on – wrenches his diffident eyes from the middle distance and sets them on Freya.

'Ciao,' he says.

'My fiancé,' Elise adds.

Your what now? Freya thinks. She looks quickly to Josh, but his face is blank. Freya recovers and nods a hello to Franco. His attention falters slightly, then drifts away, as if mere trifles like social greetings are pointless to him.

Elise smiles broadly, her lip gloss reflecting in the light. 'And you haven't RSVPed to my invite, Joshua. Did you receive it?'

'Yes, I got it,' he replies. His hand drops from Freya's shoulders; she feels suddenly cold.

'So, you're coming?' she tinkles. 'Your mum and dad can't make it, but it would be lovely to have you there. As long as you don't talk murder all night long.'

Freya looks up at Josh, who's still staring at Elise. 'I need to check my work schedule,' Josh mutters.

'Joshua's a detective, Franco. In the *police*.'

She says police with a hushed tone. Like he's in MI5 or the CIA; a dirty secret that people shouldn't discuss.

'So's Freya,' Josh replies.

Freya forces a smile.

'That's nice,' Elise replies, without conviction. 'Franco's in wine, aren't you?'

Franco doesn't reply.

'Anyway, we'd better get on,' Elise says. 'Although I don't know why we came here,' she adds. 'It's all so *high street*.'

And with that she grabs Franco's hand and swans off, high heels clacking on the tiled floor.

'So, that's Elise,' Freya says.

Josh doesn't reply but turns and walks towards the lifts. Freya follows. He's silent as they go up to the food court, as they sit down at a table, give their orders for drinks. Freya watches Josh, all his attention focused on the menu. The previous good mood has evaporated, disappeared into the air like a cloud of Elise's hairspray.

'She's not as I imagined,' Freya says. 'She's very...' She struggles to find the word. 'Glamorous.'

Josh's eyes lift. 'She's that, all right.'

'Did you know she was engaged?' Freya asks, although obviously he did. He had an invite to her wedding.

'Yes.'

'Are you going?'

'I doubt it. It's in Italy.'

'That figures. Franco must be Italian.'

'Hmm.'

Freya's aware she's chattering gormlessly, but she can't think what else to say. The actual words going round in her head are too mortifying to articulate out loud. Elise cheated on him, and yet the reason he says he's not going is because the wedding's in Italy. She's still in contact with Josh's parents, so close she invited them to her wedding, and yet Freya – his actual, current girlfriend – hasn't met them.

And bumping into Elise has completely changed Josh. He's silent. Pensive. Depressed, even. Such a difference from her usual happy-go-lucky boyfriend.

Looking at him, anyone would think he was bothered by the thought of his ex-girlfriend getting married.

Anyone would think he was still in love with her.

16

Steph is the picture of professionalism as she waits, ready to begin the post-mortem of Alex Reynolds. She holds her gloved hands out in front of her, full protective apron and mask on. The pathology technician has already prepared the body: Y incision complete.

She nods a greeting as Robin arrives. He tilts his head, trying to look at the face of the guy on the table. It's never a good idea to identify with the person about to be taken to pieces, but he's curious. The more photographs he's looked at, the more he's read the files, the more he's started to remember about Alex from around the station and the courthouse. Friendly smile. A relaxed gait to his walk, as if none of the evil acts committed by his clients could touch him. He thinks back to when he last saw him, representing the boy involved in the death of the man found in the freezer.

He'd been at the courthouse with Freya, and Alex had caught her after the final sentencing.

'It was a solid case, DC West,' he'd said. But he'd sensed she was downcast. He'd put a hand on her arm. 'You did your job. And you did it well. I hope we can work together again in the future.'

And with that, he'd left, swinging his black rucksack over his shoulder and loping off down the corridor. That was the last time Robin had seen him. Until today.

He can't see any trace of that man in the body on the table. He's clearly underweight, cheekbones protruding, arms little more than bone. He is almost completely bald, a fine dark fuzz on his skull. Regrowth after chemo, Robin assumes. Steph works quietly, directing instructions to her technician, recording notes as she goes.

He sits and waits patiently, impressed, as he often is, by Steph's obvious intelligence and ability. The contrast between her and the vapid women he's ended up with on internet dates couldn't be more pronounced.

One in particular struggled to come to terms with what he did for a living.

'You see dead bodies and stuff?' she had asked, the glass of wine hovering next to her lips.

'Sometimes.' She was in her mid-thirties and she'd seemed nice as they'd chatted briefly online. But while they talked face to face, their differences were becoming apparent.

'I couldn't bear that,' she said. 'Doesn't it get depressing?' But before he could answer, she moved on. 'I get down when I miss my ASOS order and it goes to the post office,' she continued, with a little laugh. 'I'm not sure I could cope.'

'You have no fucking idea,' he muttered, and lifted his hand to get the bill.

'Butler?' Steph's voice pulls his attention from his musings. She snaps the gloves off her hands and moves away to the side of the room. The technician takes over.

Robin stands up. 'What did you find, Steph?'

Steph pulls her mask off. 'The drugs found at his house correspond with his medical records and the state of the body on the table. Alex Reynolds had terminal cancer.' She glances back over, her face glum. 'Initially diagnosed in July as inoperable pancreatic cancer, it spread quickly to his liver and then… well, everywhere. He can't have had long to live. Maybe months.'

'Poor guy,' Robin mutters. 'So what happened on the beach?' he continues. 'What killed him?'

'A combination of factors. I found large amounts of morphine in his system, which would have lowered his respiratory rate and eventually stopped him breathing.'

'Wouldn't you expect to see that, given the drugs he was taking?'

'Yes, but not at these levels. Morphine delays gastric emptying, so – looking at stomach contents, plus taking into consideration the rate morphine metabolises in the body – I can tell he consumed a high dose, orally, less than an hour before death. And quite a substantial amount of alcohol.'

Robin frowns. 'Hardly recommended in his condition.'

'Exactly. Add both to the cold that night and his low body weight – you can see how he would have been hypothermic. His body just couldn't cope. And I have the results back from the blood tests taken at the hospital from the other victims. They've worked fast, given the suspicious circumstances.'

'The same?'

'Absolutely. Morphine found in all of them. The highest concentrations in Alex Reynolds and Michael Williams, the lowest in Meg Carlton. Again, it would have made them sleepy, which comes with the depression of respiration. Couple that with the excessive drinking and it would have knocked them out for long enough to cause the damage to Michael Williams' hands.'

'Any drugs in their system?'

'Apart from the morphine, no.'

'And how much alcohol?'

'A lot.' Steph moves over to the computer and pulls up the report. 'Given that their blood wasn't taken until they arrived at the hospital, maybe eight hours after ingestion, the levels were still considerable. Sam and Mike at 0.85, both still over the legal limit. Sara at 0.5. Meg Carlton was at zero, so she obviously drank less than the others, although we can't say how much. They should all think themselves lucky they didn't end up like Alex here.'

The two of them look to the corpse on the table.

'Any idea about TOD?' Robin asks at last.

'The body was found at seven yesterday morning. Comparing the ambient temperature to the rectal temp at the scene and his low body mass, I would estimate he died sometime between one and four a.m., but he may have been unconscious for a while before that. Did you find out the relationship between them?' she asks.

'Friends from university, judging from photographs found at his house.'

Steph sighs. 'Not such a bad way to go,' she says quietly. 'Compared with some I've seen. Slipping away, listening to the tide wash in. Body numbed with morphine and alcohol.' She looks up to him with a sad smile. 'Surrounded by your friends.'

'The aunt says suicide wasn't an option,' Robin counters.

'And you believe her? You're normally such a sceptic.'

Robin nods slowly. He thinks of his sister and nephew dying, hit by a car at a junction. His other nephew, surviving longer, hooked up to wires and machines in hospital. There are worse ways to go, he thinks morosely.

'Could it have been an accident?' he asks.

'I wondered that. I took the liberty of speaking to his oncologist. He said Alex was one of the most diligent patients he's had. Asked ten times more questions than most people. Always knew what drug regime he was on – what he should have been taking and when.' She pauses, checking the toxicology report on the screen in front of her. 'And it was a lot of morphine,' she finishes.

He thanks Steph and leaves, his head full of her words.

If he believes the aunt, Alex hasn't killed himself. If he believes the oncologist, then it wasn't an accidental death.

Take those two explanations away, Robin thinks, as he gets into his car and drives home, and what's left? Could his initial assumption be correct? Had someone set out to deliberately kill Alex Reynolds?

Was this murder?

17

Sara pauses in the doorway to the surgical ward and pinches the top of her nose between her finger and thumb. She has a headache growing, pain pulsing at the front of her brain. Mike has been transferred here; she's under instruction to bring the things he might need from home: pyjamas, toiletries, toothbrush. She's not sure what else she should have packed. The whole situation is unfathomable.

'Mrs Williams?' A doctor stops her in the doorway. She looks at the woman: young, tiny, in a neat shirt and black trousers with an NHS lanyard round her neck. She doesn't look older than mid-twenties, although Sara tells herself she must be. 'I'm Dr Kate Buchanan. I'm working on your husband's case.'

'How is he this morning?'

'Better. His body temp is back to normal, but he's been assessed as having second-degree frostbite. He has full-thickness skin freezing, a substantial build-up of fluid and swelling, plus blistering on both hands. He's in a considerable amount of pain. We're treating him with rewarming in a water bath twice daily, ibuprofen and anti-inflammatories. Plus, a tetanus jab and broad-spectrum antibiotics to be safe. We'll have to wait before we know more.'

This woman doesn't know that Sara's a doctor. That there are a million questions she could ask – about long-term prognosis, whether Mike's fingers will recover or whether they'll need to carry out debridement: a messy procedure, involving the removal of dead and damaged tissue, which might leave scars and carries a risk of infection. Whether that won't work, and he'll need them amputated. But she nods and lets the woman continue, discussing necrotic margins, pain relief, the opiates Mike is on.

'So he'll be pretty out of it when you see him today,' she concludes. She stops and Sara feels her staring. 'Are you okay?' the doctor asks. 'I know you were out there, too?'

'Yes, yes, I'm fine,' Sara says. A reply almost as automatic now as breathing. Ingrained over the years. 'Just a bit of mild hypothermia. All good now. Can I see him?'

The doctor leaves and she makes her way slowly down the ward. Many of the beds are empty, others curtained off so she can't see the unfortunate residents within. Mike is lucky, compared to these people. Lucky, and plain stupid, she thinks, feeling the flare of annoyance again. He could have just worn gloves, like she told him. A better coat. Not been such a hardened smoker, so his blood vessels could have coped. But no, he wouldn't listen to reason, especially not from her.

He's alone, at the end of the ward. His eyes are closed, his hands partially elevated, resting on pillows in front of him, white bandages obscuring the black and red skin beneath. She pauses, looking at him. The man she married, twenty years ago. The man she loved. Then.

She didn't sleep last night. She doesn't like being alone in the house, where every noise is startling, her nerves on high alert. The kids are being looked after by her parents and they'd implored her to stay, but the noise, the gaiety, seemed wrong. Alex is dead. He'd been dying already – the physical change in him had been distressing to see – but now it's over, the finality of it all has shocked her into a numbness she remembers only too well.

Alex was the peacemaker, the glue that held them together. 'You're my family,' he'd always said with a grin, a statement that made tragic sense when they found out about his parents.

They met in halls. Randomly assigned. Five bedrooms, one kitchen. Away from home for the first time, the five of them did everything together – walked to lectures, drank at the bar. Sat up, late at night, in one bedroom, just talking. They all knew people from their courses – students they worked alongside, swapped notes, chatted with – but outside of lectures it didn't occur to them to hang out with anyone else. Why would they? They had each other.

Every night they ate their meals crammed round the dining table. A tradition that stood, even in those final months.

Alex finished his exams first and started working. A shit job, maintenance on the M3 at night. But it paid well. He would return home at seven a.m., covered in dirt, and stinking of bitumen and sweat. Sara would hear the noise of the shower, his singing, deliberately loud to wake them all up.

'Breakfast,' he'd shout as he went down the stairs to the kitchen.

There was always food. Meg worked evenings at Safeway. She hated having to lock up the big gates of the car park in the dark, but she loved grabbing the discounts, first dibs on the good stuff, sold for pennies near its sell-by date. Alex clattered in the kitchen as they all emerged bleary-eyed from their bedrooms. Bacon, sausages, eggs, toast; Alex always ravenous and beanpole thin.

Shit, how she misses him.

Her phone rings, making her jump. She wipes the tears away, then pulls it out of her pocket and looks at the name on the screen. She silences it quickly. When she looks up again, Mike is awake. His eyes are drowsy, half-open.

'I've brought you some stuff,' she says, pathetically holding out the bag.

'Thanks.' His voice is thick and slow. 'How are the kids?'

'They're fine. At Mum and Dad's. I think they're going to stay there for a bit. While you're in here.' He nods, his eyes closing for a moment. 'I'll bring them in to see you,' she finishes. 'When you're feeling a bit better.'

He makes a noise, halfway between a laugh and a snarl. 'Don't trouble yourself.'

'Mike—'

'This must suit you. Me in here. Out of your way.'

'That's not—'

'Was that always your plan?' he growls.

'I didn't—'

'Whatever, Sara,' he slurs. He closes his eyes, and this time doesn't open them again. 'Good luck coping on your own.'

She stares at him a moment longer, then gently places the bag on the chair next to his bed. Twenty years, she thinks as she leaves. Twenty years, and it ends like this.

18

'Honestly, Mina, it was like she had crawled straight from the pages of *Vogue*.'

Freya's at home, slumped in front of the muted TV. At the other end of the phone, Mina laughs. Freya imagines Mina sat on her own sofa, kids' toys scattered around her, head tilted sideways in the sympathetic look Freya has seen a thousand times before. The only female DCs in Major Crimes, they'd met nearly seven years ago and bonded over a shared refusal to make the tea or take notes, rolling their eyes as men called them 'darling' or 'love'. Mina's personal favourite – 'doll' – was a source of many a disparaging retort. ('What am I, a plastic toy?' Mina would say, accompanied by Freya's barely concealed splutter of laughter. 'I don't have the boobs to be a Barbie, for a start.')

'She can't have been that bad?' Mina replies now.

'Oh, she was. It's no wonder Josh moved down from Newcastle for her.' Freya picks up the glass of wine from her coffee table. 'What am I going to do?' she wails.

'How did you leave it?' In the background Freya can hear the cry of a small child, followed by a man's voice trying to placate the screaming.

'I invited him back here but he said he was tired.'

'Perhaps he was,' Mina suggests gently.

'Josh is never tired. The man's a human Duracell Bunny.'

'Lucky you.'

'I didn't mean like that. I meant...' Freya groans softly. 'What if he goes back to her? I can't compete with that.'

'Freya, you're not supposed to.' Another yowl of anguish from a child. 'Leave him alone,' Mina shouts. 'Leave. Him. Alone.' A sigh, and she comes back on the phone. 'He spent Christmas with you, didn't he?'

'Yes,' Freya agrees reluctantly.

'There you go. What did he get you?'

Freya pauses. 'A jumper. And...' She knows Mina's going to have an opinion about her other present.

'And?'

'Football tickets. To a Newcastle game. Next month.'

There's a long silence.

'To the team that *he* supports?' Mina says slowly. 'In winter?'

'Yes, okay, okay,' she replies, defensive. 'It was nice. He said we could go together. And we could visit his parents at the same time.'

'Wow. This gets better and better.'

'Okay, enough with the sarcasm,' Freya laughs. 'Presents aren't his strong suit.'

'What did you get him?'

'This Marvel thing he's been going on about. A khaki-brown jacket, with *Variant* on the back, and the TVA logo on the front.'

Silence again. 'I don't get it.'

'No, me neither. But Josh said it was limited edition. Collectors' item, apparently.'

And it had cost a bloody fortune. Freya hadn't believed it when she'd seen the price tag. But the look on his face had been worth it.

She hears another blood-curdling scream. Mina groans. 'I've got to go. The kids are trying to kill each other. Whoever said that Christmases with children are full of joy and wonderment was having a fucking joke. All I want right now is to get back to work for some peace and quiet.'

Freya laughs. 'See you Tuesday.'

'Can't come soon enough,' Mina replies, and hangs up.

Freya sighs and looks at her phone. Still no reply from Josh. She's never seen him like that before, so distracted. So uninterested in her. But she doesn't want to push it, so before she cracks and texts him again, she forces herself to put her mobile down on the table.

She picks up the box full of the photos taken from Alex's house, now placed carefully in an evidence bag. She told Robin she'd look through them, the least she could do given she'd left him to go to the post-mortem alone.

She clears the table, then spreads them out across the wooden surface. There's a lot. Some of them are in their original paper envelopes, negatives tucked at the front, others loose. Relics from a different age: when you had to remember to bring a camera out with you, 35mm film loaded into the back and then taken to Boots for developing. The shots are grainy, yellowed with age. But all are unmistakably showing the same group.

Freya smiles at the photos, remnants of a bygone era. Mismatched soft furnishings, cushions and curtains bought on the cheap or borrowed from parents' houses. Half-filled ashtrays, mess and debris surrounding people with more fun things to do than clean. The photos show the boys playing computer games, a youthful Alex with his mouth half-open in concentration. A woman with dark hair, Meg, lying in an overgrown garden reading a book.

Carefree times.

But always the same five. Never anyone else in the photo. And that's odd. Freya remembers her own time at university. Hanging out with her housemates, yes, but also acquaintances from her course, friends of friends, people she might have met once on a night out.

Freya squints at one photo and picks it up. A blurry close-up selfie in the foreground, but in the back, two others, cuddled up on the sofa, cheeks pressed together. She shuffles the deck, finds another. This time they're in a nightclub, snogging. No doubt about it now.

Her phone beeps, making her jump. Her first thought: Josh! But she's disappointed; it's only Robin with an update from the PM.

COD: hypothermia, opiate overdose, compounded by terminal cancer.

Then a follow-up text: *How was shopping??*

Bloody awful, she thinks. She gets an urge to speak to him, tell him what she's found. She's up from the sofa, already anticipating his slight smile, the wrinkle of his forehead, watching her quietly as she shares her thoughts on the case.

If her own boyfriend can't bear to text tonight, at least Robin will be glad to see her.

19

Favours, they need all the bloody favours. Robin's home after the post-mortem; the smell of disinfectant lingers in his nose, appetite lost. He texts Freya the cause of death, then goes for a shower.

Clean, dressed, he picks up his phone and notices a missed call from her. Interesting, he thinks. He assumed she'd be with Josh tonight, as she is most days. But he doesn't return her call, looking for another number first.

'This better be an invite to the pub,' Greg says, straight away. One of the analysts in the Digital team, he's always been Robin's go-to guy, despite his abrupt manner.

Robin pauses. 'It could be...'

'But?'

He collapses on the sofa, preparing for Greg's excuses. 'I need someone from Intel to do some work for me tomorrow—'

'And you don't know any of them.' Greg sighs. Robin can hear the television in the background – loud bangs and electronic zips – and knows Greg will be watching the latest sci-fi offering on Netflix. 'Fine. I'll make a call. But it better be something they can do remotely. There's no way you'll get any of those sods to the office on the day after Boxing Day. In *snow*.'

Robin glances out of the window. Sure enough, white flakes scatter again against the black sky and he wonders how much is forecast, whether the world will be functioning when he wakes up in the morning.

'Thanks, Greg. Are you in tomorrow?'

'Yes. Why?' He's suspicious, and he is right to be.

'There's a mobile phone I need you to look at as priority.' Robin hears a ring from the front door and gets up, the phone clamped to his ear as he talks to Greg. 'It'll be on your desk, first thing.'

'I can't wait,' Greg replies, his voice dripping with disdain. 'Send me the info for Intel. And let me get back to consuming my body weight in fried food. Please.'

Robin hangs up then opens the front door. He's surprised to see Freya there, woolly pink scarf wrapped up to her nose, matching hat pulled down low over her ears.

'So, I had a thought,' she says without greeting. He smiles – he really does miss her when she's not around – and moves out of her way. She hurries inside. 'I've been looking through these photos. Sara Williams is married to Mike, right?'

'Yes. The bloke with frostbite.'

They both walk through to his living room, Freya pulling her coat and scarf off as she goes. She slumps down on his sofa, moving the papers and empty glasses from his coffee table without comment and placing her bag on top.

'Well, I don't think he was her first choice at uni.' She pauses for effect.

'Go on...'

She pulls out the photographs and shows him one. 'See here? In all these shots she was with—'

'Sam Bowen,' Robin finishes. He looks closely at the photo. The two of them look different: Sara's hair over her shoulders, thick and long. Sam's face plump with the puppy fat of youth. But definitely the same people.

'Exactly. Our favourite psychology doc. See here?' She shows him another and Robin shrinks from the almost graphic display of affection. 'Snogging his face off. They were definitely together.'

Robin agrees with her assessment. 'You're thinking there was some sort of love triangle going on?'

'Maybe. Why don't we visit? Put this in front of her. I'm curious what she'll say.'

'Sure. Tomorrow. Since we're still not allowed near Mike Williams. Whacked up on drugs,' he explains to Freya's questioning look. 'Plus, we need to interview Meg Carlton. And I spoke to Greg. He says he can rope in someone from Intel to help us.'

'Greg from Digital?' Freya asks. 'Nerdy Greg, who stares at my tits when he thinks I'm not looking?'

'That's the one. And I didn't realise he did that.'

'Why do you think I always make you speak to him?'

'Authority?'

Freya scoffs. 'And we're still thinking this death is suspicious?' she continues. 'Even given what caused it? We know he was on morphine.'

Robin relays what the oncologist had told Steph. That Alex was diligent about his medicine.

'And the aunt was pretty sure it wasn't deliberate,' Freya finishes. She pauses, staring into space.

'What?' Robin asks.

'I kind of feel like… I don't know.' Freya sighs. 'That we should do all we can, for Alex. We're always thorough,' she adds quickly. 'But we should go the extra mile on this one. Make doubly sure. We knew him, after all.'

Robin nods in agreement. 'We will, Frey. I promise. We have the CCTV to check, and the mobile phone. We won't get Baker to downgrade it until we're a hundred per cent convinced there's nothing dodgy going on.' She smiles, a look of relief. 'Anyway, Freya, what are you doing here? Aren't you with Bruce Wayne tonight?'

'We don't spend every second of every day together,' she comments, and gets up and walks into the kitchen. Robin notes the change in tone. Trouble in paradise? he wonders. He hears the fridge opening and the fizz of a bottle of beer. 'Do you want one?' she shouts, out of sight.

'Of my own beer?' he replies with a grin. 'Go on then.'

She comes back into the room and hands him the bottle, sinking down next to him. 'Have you caught up on series six yet?' she asks.

'Episode four.'

'Want to watch it?'

He smiles. 'Sure.'

They spend the next few hours together. As the snow falls silently outside; as the Christmas weekend draws to a close. Robin lies on one side of the sofa, socked feet resting on the coffee table. Freya next to him, scruffy in tracksuit bottoms and a sweatshirt, periodically distracted by the silent phone next to her. She looks through the photographs, every now and again showing one to Robin.

He enjoys the quiet moments like these. Even more so with Freya. He looks at the pictures of Alex Reynolds, clearly happy with his friends, and wonders why he'd been so alone in his life. Where were the rest of his friends now? Once again, he finds himself drawing comparisons between Alex and himself. Robin was once like this, he thinks, looking at the candid shots of a life lived without worry at university. Laughing, drinking, chatting about shit to no one in particular. He knows what happened in his own life, and now wonders whether the same had impacted Alex's. A death, a trauma, a tragedy? A secret? Something so big it rips you apart. Rendering you incapable of functioning like a proper human being, forming loving relationships without doubting every single fucking thing that comes out of your mouth.

He looks over at Freya. What is it about her that means he can completely be himself? He doesn't care that she's turned up unannounced. That she sees him like this: hair unbrushed, house a mess, unshaven. A small dribble of toothpaste on his jumper from last night. She catches his glance, beer bottle halfway to her mouth.

'What?' she grins.

But he can't say that. Never would. Instead, he points to the television.

'Skip the intro, will you,' he comments. 'Remote's closest to you.'

She does as she's asked and goes back to her beer. They watch the next episode. Silent, content.

No personal questions, no complications. Keeping each other company the only way they know how.

20

Monday

The Williams family live in a part of town known for its nice schools and house prices to match. Robin drives slowly down the tree-lined road, where residences loom large with big gardens and driveways.

'Eighteen, there it is,' Freya points, and Robin pulls up outside.

Christmas lights adorn the front – tacky and dull in the dim glow of the winter's day. The soft dusting of snow that had fallen overnight now lies as brown slush on the concrete.

Freya's always wanted a place like this. A family home. Detached. Nice neighbours, good catchment area. The idea of living somewhere like this with Josh briefly crosses her mind but she dismisses it. They haven't spoken since yesterday, her texts still going unanswered.

She'd left Robin's just past eleven last night, after one beer and two cups of tea. She hadn't been able to eat that morning, Josh's silence gnawing at her stomach.

'Are you going to tell me what's going on?' Robin asks. He's sensed her mood and been silent for most of the drive, but now he stops and turns towards her. 'With you and Josh?'

'It's nothing.'

'It's clearly something.'

'I...' She rolls the words round in her head. She would like to talk about it with Robin; maybe a man's perspective would help. But not now. 'Later,' she tells him.

He nods silently and looks up to the house. Lights are on in a few of the rooms; a car sits idle in the driveway.

'Are you ready? I think someone's home.'

She opens the car door. The street is quiet, bar the steady drip of snow melting from the trees and the crunch of ice underfoot. It's so cold; she pushes her hands into the pockets of her coat for the short walk up to the door.

She follows Robin along the driveway, taking small steps on the frozen ground. He rings the doorbell. After a pause, it's opened by a small boy – Freya guesses about ten years old – with a shock of bright blond hair. He stares at them.

Robin shows him his warrant card. 'Hampshire Police,' he says. 'Is your mum in?'

The boy stares at it, open-mouthed. Then he shouts, without taking his eyes off Robin, 'Mum! Police!'

Sara Williams appears quickly behind him. Having spent so long looking at the photos last night, Freya's struck by the difference in hairstyles. While Sara's hair at university was long, wavy, glossy, now it's short, barely past her ears, and styled into harsh, straight lines.

'Freddy, go in the house—'

'But Mum—'

'Now!' The boy reluctantly turns and skulks away. Sara Williams makes no effort to invite them in, her arm blocking the door. 'I don't want you here,' she says.

'Mrs Williams,' Robin begins pleasantly. 'If we could have five minutes of your time?'

'I have nothing else to tell you.'

'We only want the same as you: to find out what happened to your husband and Alex.'

Sara pauses, scowling. Then she shifts to the side, a slight movement, barely giving ground. 'Five minutes,' she says.

They walk into the house, but Sara Williams doesn't progress any further than the hallway. Freya can see through into the other rooms: a plush sitting room to their left, an open plan kitchen diner in front, grey day streaming in through the skylight. Robin gives her a little nudge. *You try*, he's saying.

'I'm DC Freya West,' Freya begins with a smile. 'Could you tell us what happened on Christmas Eve?'

'Haven't we covered this already?' Short. Sharp.

'Yes, but we would like to go over it again.'

Silence.

'How do you know the other people that were there on Christmas Eve?' Freya tries again.

'Why is that important?'

'For background. In case it shows motive behind how you all ended up unconscious.'

'There's no motive.' She pauses. Freya waits. 'We're friends from university,' she says eventually, with a sigh. A shadow passes across Sara's face, and she lowers her gaze to the ground. She seems tired, dark circles under her heavily made-up eyes.

Robin fidgets next to her. 'Can I use your toilet?' he asks.

Sara frowns at him, then points up the stairs. 'Second door on the right.'

She watches Robin as he heads up, going into the room she pointed towards. Satisfied, she turns back to Freya.

'Will this take long? We're only here to collect clothes for the kids. I need to get to the hospital.'

'How is your husband?' Freya asks softly.

Sara chews on the inside of her lip. 'The doctors are monitoring him closely. They're hoping they'll be able to save most of his damaged fingers.'

'I'm sorry. It must be hard.'

'What? To have your husband in hospital on Christmas Day? To tell your kids that Daddy isn't going to be home to open his presents? Your friend, dead—' She stops abruptly. 'What are you investigating this as?'

Freya hesitates. She remembers that Mike Williams used to be a cop and assumes that Sara is used to the terminology.

'A suspicious death,' she replies. 'Until we know more.'

Sara's face is stern. 'None of us did this,' she says.

'Was there anyone else there that night?'

'No, but… I know these people.'

'You're friends,' Freya repeats.

'Yes.'

'And Sam Bowen?'

At that, her face freezes. 'Friends,' she says at last.

They hear a door close. Footsteps as Robin descends the stairs and joins Freya.

'Were you close to anyone else at university?' Freya continues. 'Anyone from your course? Didn't you work in a pub? You must have met loads of people there?'

She feels Robin's eyes on her, inquisitive.

'How do you know about my job?'

'Photos,' Freya replies. 'Recovered from Alex's house. Did you have friends there, too?'

'Why does that matter?' Sara's voice is cold and Freya considers how long they have before she kicks them out.

'I'm wondering if there was anyone else at your gathering on Christmas Eve. Someone who left before the ambulance turned up?'

Sara glares. 'Stop fishing, Detective,' she replies. 'You find a few snapshots from twenty years ago and you think you know everything about my life. About my brief relationship with Sam.' She emphasises the words *brief relationship*. 'And no,' Sara continues. 'There wasn't anyone else there. Not from the pub, or Alex's job on the roads, or Meg's checkout shifts at Safeway. Are you done?'

'Will you come into the station for a voluntary interview?'

'No. I'm not setting foot in that police station unless you arrest me.'

'We're not going to arrest you, Mrs Williams,' Robin says gently, trying to placate the woman.

She walks to the front door and holds it open. 'Then I want you to go.'

Freya nods, and follows Robin's lead, leaving the house. The door slams shut and they walk back to the car. Robin quickly starts the engine and turns the heat up.

'What did she say while I was upstairs?' Robin asks.

Freya fills him in on their conversation. 'I'm not sure it helps much. Did you get anything from your snoop?'

He smiles, smug. It's the oldest trick in the book. Feign the need for the bathroom and have a good old look around while you're up there.

'Not much. Upstairs was the same. Neat, tidy. Expensive.' His phone rings and he looks at it. 'Although I did notice a whole load of packing boxes in the spare room. Someone moving out?'

'Or a clear-out?' she suggests. 'Trying to get rid of the past?'

Robin answers his phone. 'Greg, give me something, please.'

Freya watches as he listens. She's starting to think they're wasting their time here. It was no more than an unfortunate accident: Alex dosing his own drink for comfort, the others wanting an innocuous try of hard drugs.

'Thanks, Greg.' Robin hangs up and turns to Freya. 'He has something from the phone. Wants to show us back at the nick.'

But he doesn't put the car into gear. Robin pauses, his face lit up. She can tell he has something else to share.

'Go on then,' she prompts, humouring him. 'Tell me.'

'I did see this. Took a quick photo. Here.'

He holds out his phone and she takes it. The photo on the screen is a formal shot from a wedding, the bride and groom in the middle Sara and Mike Williams.

'And?' Freya asks.

'Zoom in. Take a closer look at the guests.' He waits while she squints at the screen. After a moment, she looks back up, confused.

'I give up, Robin. What are you getting at?'

He grins. 'Who's not there?'

Her mouth opens and she looks back down to the photo. 'The other three,' she says at last.

'Exactly,' Robin replies. He puts the car into gear and starts to drive. 'If they were such good friends, Freya, why were none of them at their wedding?'

21

'I mean, fuck, how can I even compete with that?'

They're walking down to see Greg, and it seems that now Freya has started talking, she can't stop. Robin's been silent throughout the car journey, his involvement in the conversation assumed optional.

Robin had predicted a shopping trip between Freya and Josh would end in disaster. Mainly because no normal man wants to be dragged round endless hot, busy clothes shops and asked seemingly innocent questions like, 'Do you like this?' which apparently have a right and a wrong answer which isn't the one you expect. But that wasn't the problem. No, it was meeting the ex. Or, more specifically, Josh's reaction to her.

'I don't think—' Robin begins, but Freya's on a roll. Twenty minutes of in depth explanation in the car have felt like an eternity. Bloody hell, he wishes he'd never asked.

'She's six foot tall, completely gorgeous, looks like she's never eaten a Twirl in her life.' That last comment is directed at the chocolate bar in Freya's own hand, and she pushes the wrapper into her pocket in disgust. 'And the way her fiancé looked at us! Like we were shit on his shoe.'

'Sounds like Josh is better off without her,' Robin tries again.

'Well, I wish he felt that way. He got a wedding invite from her. Did I mention that?'

'A few times,' he mutters, but she ignores him.

'Why hasn't he told me? He says he's not going to go, but what if it's because he still loves her? Why is she still in touch with his parents? What if he wants her back? What if,' she says, her voice rising to a mildly hysterical squeak, 'she wants *him* back?'

'I'm sure it's fine,' Robin says. But she just glares. This reassurance thing isn't his forte. 'Why don't you speak to Mina?' he suggests.

'I already have.'

'And?'

'She said not to worry.'

'There you go then.'

Freya quietens as Robin pushes the door open into the Digital team's office. He has a coffee in his hand, hopeful that a bit of bribery will smooth the way.

Greg is sitting on the far side of the room. Unlike those belonging to the rest of his team, his desk is completely empty, bar two massive screens and a variety of wires criss-crossing the tabletop. He looks up as Robin and Freya approach and, shit, Freya's right. Greg's gaze immediately drops to her chest. Robin debates withdrawing the coffee, but he's seen it now and is holding out his hand.

Robin passes it across and Greg takes a sip then puts it behind him, far away from the precious electronics.

'I expect at least one of these a day from now on,' Greg comments.

'Expect all you like,' Robin replies. 'Doesn't mean it's going to happen. But thank you,' he adds quickly, 'for having a go at this phone as priority.'

Greg raises a finger. 'Don't thank me yet, I've only been going at it for a few hours. Barely made it through the unlock screen.'

'But you have something?'

'Would I have called otherwise?'

'If you wanted coffee, yes.'

Greg smiles. 'True. But yes, I have found something.' Robin and Freya crowd behind Greg; he pulls out a chair and Freya sits down, while Robin remains standing, squinting at the text on the screen.

'So, I had a look for the names you mentioned. Checking his contacts, text messages, that sort of thing. And there's a lot of activity.'

'Really?' Robin's surprised. Perhaps this lot were friends, after all.

'But only over the last three weeks. It all started on the eighth of December – Reynolds sent an email to all of them… Here.'

He points. An array of email addresses, all clearly belonging to the other four. The message, vague but purposeful: *I'm sorry to contact you after all this time. We need to talk, call me. Please. Alex x*

And then his mobile number.

'And did they?' Freya asks. 'Call?'

'Not straight away,' Greg replies. 'A few more messages go back and forth. Basically, all refusing. Sara Williams was a bit more placatory, saying something about a promise. Sam Bowen seems to have blocked him. Michael Williams doesn't reply at all.'

'And then what?'

'I don't know. But he's managed to get a mobile number for Megan Carlton because he calls her. Here, on the twenty-first of December. That's her number.'

Robin looks. They spoke for ten minutes. Then, two days later, on the twenty-third of December, she calls him back. Shorter this time. One minute and thirty-six seconds.

'Arranging a meet-up?' Robin suggests to Freya. 'Meg was the mediator? Sorting time and date with the others?'

'And this…' Greg says.

They turn back to the screen and Greg clicks on an audio file. It hisses, then a voice fills the air.

'We're on our way. Kids were a nightmare.' The voice is female and abrupt. Distinctly unfriendly. 'Don't agree anything without us.'

'That was Sara Williams,' Greg says, switching it off. 'Left at 8.24 p.m. on Christmas Eve. Alex Reynolds didn't even pick it up.'

Robin nods slowly, processing all they've learned. So the five of them hadn't been in touch. But something had prompted Alex Reynolds to message.

'He was dying and wanted to make amends?' Freya suggests when they're out in the corridor, after leaving Greg with assurances of more coffee and a Danish if he makes more progress before the case conference tomorrow morning.

'Could be. But for what? What could have caused five close friends to stop speaking to each other for twenty years?'

Freya shrugs. Robin looks at her. She seems downcast, her mind obviously on other things. Josh-related things.

'You know,' Robin says. 'You could always ask him.' Freya stares. 'Josh,' he continues. 'You could just ask him why he hadn't told you about the wedding. And why he seems so upset.'

She stops in the corridor, mouth open slightly. 'Do you think he'll tell me?'

Robin tilts his head to one side, sympathetically. 'He's a bloke, Freya. I haven't got much in common with Mr Incredible, but I can guess he's not giving this whole thing as much analysis as you are. I'm sure it's something straightforward and boring. Ask him.'

She nods slowly, and the two start walking again.

'What's next then, Robin?' Freya asks. 'With the case. Where do you want to take it?'

He stops, thinking. 'We need to check the CCTV, make sure there wasn't anyone else there. Chase the lab for the forensics on the exhibits taken at the scene, plus the pharmaceuticals collected from Alex's house. We have the case conference tomorrow and Baker is going to want to see something useful. And I want to speak to Meg Carlton. Let's bring her in for an interview. Voluntarily, of course,' he says with a grin. 'Did Alex's office come back to you?'

'Yes,' Freya replies. 'They said we can go over any time we like.'

'Call them back, let's go now. And hopefully by tomorrow we'll have more of a complete picture.'

They walk back into the office, and as they do, Robin notices Freya's face flush. Josh is on the opposite side of the room, talking to a DC. He's laughing at something they're saying, a cup of coffee in his hand. To Robin he seems the same annoying bloke he's always been.

'See?' Freya hisses as they pick up their coats. 'Something's wrong.'

Robin shakes his head with disbelief. 'You know, Freya. This is a new side of you.'

'What do you mean?'

'Needy, insecure. Never noticed it before. Interesting to see.'

'I'm not… Oh, piss off,' she finishes, striding out of the office in front of him.

He laughs softly. Perhaps he is better off single after all.

22

Robin was expecting shiny chrome and glass sliding doors, so is mildly disappointed when he's faced with an office strongly reminiscent of their own incident room. He has to try hard not to scowl when a chipped mug is placed in his hands. Where's the swanky coffee machine? he ponders. A mocha-choca hazelnut-infused creation would have really made his day.

'Thank you,' Freya says warmly on receipt of her own coffee, and the man – the senior partner at the law firm of Coombes and Rosewood, David Coombes himself – smiles back.

'We were so sad to hear of Alex's passing,' he says as he sits down. 'Although surprised to hear from the police. And detectives, at that.'

'Did you know about his cancer?' Robin asks.

'Yes. Alex shared the news early on. He knew he'd have to have chemo. Time off. He even offered to resign, so as not to impinge on our good nature.'

'And did he?'

'Of course not. We kept him on full pay, even when the sickness policy ran out.'

The three of them are sitting in a conference room, around one end of a large wooden table. Like the rest of the office, it's worn: the Formica so chipped that the MDF shows through, rings from years of hot coffee mugs ingrained on the surface. David Coombes sits in front of them. His suit is wrinkled; his tie is red, checked and dating from a whole different era. A few strands of hair drift in the breeze, lonely and abandoned on the top of his otherwise bald head.

'How long did Alex work here?'

Coombes smiles. 'Since his first internship, when he was a student. Doing the filing, making the tea. But he turned into quite the criminal lawyer. We'll miss him. He was an integral part of our team.'

'Did he mention what he was doing for Christmas?' Freya asks.

'No, he always kept to himself. I know he didn't have much in the way of family.'

'And when did you see Alex last?'

'Just over a week ago. Evening of the seventeenth. I popped round his house to drop off his Christmas hamper.'

'How did he seem? Mentally and physically?'

'Tired. In pain. But in good spirits. I stayed for half an hour or so, just chatting on the sofa.'

'Was there any indication that Alex was down or depressed?' Freya asks. 'That he might have been thinking about taking his own life?'

'Alex? No. Absolutely not.' Coombes pauses. 'Is that how he died?'

Freya looks to Robin, as the senior detective, to answer.

'We're investigating,' Robin replies. 'It's early days.'

'But for detectives from Major Crimes to be involved? You must be considering other options.'

Robin smiles, tightly. 'Yes, we believe his death could be suspicious.'

'Well! Well, I never. Well...'

Robin clears his throat, trying to redirect the lawyer's thoughts to the matter at hand.

'And what can you tell us about Alex's friends? Private life?'

'Well, that's exactly it, Alex kept very private. He didn't mention any girlfriends, never brought anyone to the law dinners or functions. Not that he didn't have interest, oh no! Alex was a good-looking lad. Plenty of the ladies around here would have liked a chance, but he didn't seem keen.'

Robin idly wonders if Alex Reynolds was gay, keeping it quiet from his employers.

'Do you know if he had a will?' he asks instead.

'Yes, definitely. Held by our very own probate department.'

'I don't suppose we could have sight of that, could we?'

The lawyer grins. 'Not without the correct paperwork, DS Butler, as you very well know.'

Robin smiles back. It was worth a try. He makes a mental note to apply for a warrant when they get back to the station. 'Was there anyone who threatened him over the years?' he continues. 'Disgruntled clients, that sort of thing?'

Coombes thinks. 'Not anything that Alex mentioned.'

Sensing they're not going to get much more of interest from this guy, Robin decides to move on. 'Can we see his office?'

The man laughs. 'Desk, more like. The work we do, Detective, there's not a lot of money flying around. We're a small firm. We can barely afford this place.' He stands up, gestures out of the conference room. 'Come this way.'

The man isn't kidding. The office is run-down, in desperate need of a refresh. Brown stains seep ominously across the white ceiling tiles. The carpet is a worn race track around the splintering brown desks. The chairs are all shapes and sizes, clearly cobbled together over the years at a discount; large grey metal filing cabinets bulge with paper; bookshelves are stuffed with law tomes, their covers deep red, dark green, dusty and worn.

Few of the solicitors are in; only a couple of heads poke up from the desks as Robin and Freya walk through.

'Family law over there, conveyancing, tax, commercial.' He points in their general direction. 'And here's Alex,' Coombes announces. 'Crime. It literally doesn't pay,' he adds with a chuckle.

Robin can see what he's saying. There's no glamour here. On one side, a bulging filing tray; on the other a row of books, all with grand-sounding legal names. A computer screen sits in the middle, cables trailing. Robin pulls at the drawers underneath. They're locked.

'Do you have a key for this?' he asks. 'And the filing cabinets.' He points to the row of full height roller doors behind them.

'Yes. I'll get them.' The lawyer bustles off, leaving them in peace.

Freya sits down, twirling slightly on the swivel chair. She points at the screen. 'Did we find a laptop?'

'Not that I remember.' He picks up a copy of the *Law Society Gazette* and places it on the pile with the others, all still in their plastic wrappers. 'So, no family, no friends. Except these guys he knew at university.'

He watches as Freya flicks through the filing tray, then she stops. She pulls a red folder out and he sees what she's noticed. *WILLIAMS* is written on the side. She glances up to him and opens it.

The file is thin: what seems to be a checklist, barely completed, on the top, more paper below. Freya lifts up the first sheet of paper, then turns it around to show him.

> Application for a divorce, dissolution or (judicial) separation.

'Who's applying?' Robin asks.

She turns to the next page.

'Michael Williams.'

'Well, shit. She kept that quiet,' Robin comments.

'Perhaps she didn't know. Although it would explain the packing boxes in the spare room. Here, look.'

She turns the file round. Section 6, the reason for the divorce: adultery.

'With whom? Does it say?'

More flicking. 'No. He left it blank,' Freya replies, and Robin scowls. 'And it hasn't been signed yet.'

David Coombes reappears with a handful of keys, drops them on the desk with a clatter and starts trying them in the lock. After a few, one turns, and the drawer opens. He does the same with the filing cabinets next to them, then looks at Freya.

'What have you got there?' he asks. 'That's a family case. See, red file.'

'Divorce paperwork,' Freya replies. 'For one of Alex's friends. We found it on his desk. In plain sight,' she adds quickly. 'Why would a criminal lawyer be doing a divorce case? Would he even have the expertise?'

Coombes puts out his hand and Freya passes it across. He looks through the pages, deep in thought. 'Alex would have done a seat in family as part of his training contract. To get a proper understanding and knowledge of the law.

But that would have been over fifteen years ago now. Oh, here, that explains it.' He looks up and smiles. 'These are Rebecca's initials. One of the associate solicitors in the family department. She must have been helping him.' He smiles indulgently. 'Alex doing a bit of a freebie on the side. That was so like him.'

He pauses, hands on his hips. Robin and Freya wait for him to leave. At last Coombes clocks their expressions and makes his excuses.

Robin pulls on a pair of gloves and starts looking through. The top drawer is mainly stationery: paper clips, half-dead pens, sticky notes – those arrow-shaped ones that Robin remembers having to sign next to when his parents died. Rolls of pink ribbon and tape. Bundles of elastic bands, a stapler with *TIM* Tippexed on the top. Poor Tim, Robin thinks flippantly. Motive? Maybe. Who knows how angry Tim got over his missing stapler.

'So Mike Williams had been in touch with Alex,' Freya says as they continue their search. He glances behind him: she has opened the set of rolling doors and is looking at the full-height filing cabinet.

'I guess so. But why? He could have gone to any old solicitor out there.'

Robin moves down to the next drawer. A few files are in here, stacks of buff cardboard folders, names written down the sides. They're all stuffed full of paper, handwritten notes, typed documents.

Freya is still looking at the filing cabinet. Bulging sleeves, like the ones in the drawer, are suspended in hanging files. There must be hundreds in there.

Freya catches his eye. 'There's no way we can go through all of these.'

'No. Agreed. If we're even allowed. But let's check the PNC when we get back. In case he reported anyone for harassment or threatening behaviour over the years. Maybe someone drugged them somehow.'

She nods and turns back, pushing the files to and fro.

Robin changes position, his attention still with the drawer. Sitting cross-legged, he pulls out the pile of folders and places it in his lap. More files, more paperwork. A few A4 blue pads, reminding Robin of their investigation notebooks. He opens a few, half-used, and flicks through, looking for anything of interest. Nothing. He turns to the next, opens the blue cover and stops.

'Freya, look at this,' he says. He doesn't turn around, his eyes locked on the page.

'Hmm?' He hears Freya crouch behind him. She takes a quick intake of breath.

'But that's... Why?'

'You have no idea?'

'No.'

'He didn't call you in July?'

'No.' She shakes her head again. 'No.'

He looks up at her, her face pale. Then back to the notepad. Because written at the top of the front page, in what he's come to recognise as Alex Reynolds' handwriting is a date: 2 July 21. Six months ago. And below it, Freya's name.

For the attention of Detective Constable Freya West, it says. *Private and Confidential.*

But the page below is blank.

23

Oh god, oh god, oh god. Why did she agree to come here? Why didn't she refuse? But when that copper showed up at her door, and asked her nicely if she could accompany him down to the station, Meg didn't feel like she could say no. She hadn't even hesitated when they'd asked permission to take her DNA and prints, just let them crack on like the sap she is.

She fidgets in her uncomfortable plastic chair. Her eyes scan the room, again. Nervously taking in the black domes of the cameras on the ceiling, the recording equipment on the table. She picks up the pen, clicks it, then puts it down on the paperwork. All obediently signed, saying she understood the caution, she gave permission to be videoed.

She hears talking outside the door, followed by a quick burst of laughter. She feels a prickle of jealousy, a feeling resurrected from her schooldays. They're talking, laughing about *her*. She tells herself to calm down. You'll be fine, Meg. You'll be fine.

The door opens, and she pulls on a smile. They introduce themselves but she remembers them from Christmas Day, from the hospital. Have they forgotten her? Already? It was only two days ago – is she that unremarkable?

They sit opposite her. The blonde one shuffles papers in a file. It's quite thick. What do they know? Meg wonders. They can't, surely? Not already?

The woman asks a question. In her panic, Meg misses it, asks her to repeat herself.

'And you're happy to be here without legal advice?' West asks.

'Yes. Of course. No problem.' Meg's been asked a few times now, but each time has turned it down. To ask for a lawyer makes her seem guilty, doesn't it? Innocent people don't need lawyers.

'Fine. Let's begin. Interview started at…' the detective glances up to the clock on the wall, 'fifteen forty-five.' West smiles warmly. 'Let's go from the beginning. How did you all know each other?'

'We were friends at uni,' Meg replies.

'How close were you?' The detective reaches across with a photo; Meg takes it. She looks at it closely, remembering that day. They'd just moved in, grinning broadly outside the house. They'd felt like such adults. Their own place, the five of them. She turns it over, feeling a red blush creeping up from the collar of her cardigan as she reads what Alex had written on the back.

'The Five?' West prompts.

'That's what they called us,' Meg says. Another swell of sadness, threatening to break her. The same way it had twenty years ago. 'People round university,' she continues, wistfully. 'Because we were always together. We were so close, back then.'

'So close you didn't go to Sara and Mike's wedding?' Butler says.

Meg looks up with a jolt. 'You know about that?'

'Why didn't you go?'

'We just… I don't know. Grew apart after uni.' It's a crap answer, and the male detective knows it, staring at her for a moment. But she keeps quiet and he lets it go.

'But you were together again on Friday night?'

'Yes.'

'Because?'

She stops, blinking. She feels like a rabbit caught in the headlights. Waiting for crunch time, certain death.

'We thought it would be nice,' she manages. 'Catch up.'

'But why there?'

'Tradition.'

'Tradition?'

'Yes. We used to go there a lot. Head down in Sam's car, the five of us, all crammed in.' Alex had suggested it on the phone, just before Christmas, and she'd suspected why. A bit of nostalgia, keen to get them remembering why they'd all liked each other in the first place. Anything to dispel the bad feeling flowing bitterly between them.

'What about relationships? Were any of you together?'

Meg frowns. She doesn't like this now. Sam had said to keep quiet, but here she is, running her mouth off in an overheated interview room. But the detectives, they know stuff. A thought confirmed as the woman passes across another photograph, one showing Sara and Sam. 'Yes. Those two,' Meg confirms. 'From the beginning.'

Meg catches a glance thrown between the two detectives. Triumph. She curses herself. Shut up, shut up, shut up.

'When did Sara and Mike get together?' the woman asks.

'I'm not sure. Right at the end. After the grad ball, I think. Listen, do I need to be here?' she says quickly. 'Sara says we shouldn't be talking to the police. That you'll twist our words.'

'And what do you think, Meg?' the man asks. He sits forward slightly, resting his arms on the tabletop. His features are concerned, kind. He's attractive, she thinks, the thought intrusive and distracting. Nice eyes: a sort of green-brown. She wonders if he's single – an automatic thought, reinforced over twenty years of looking for the right man. But not now, she thinks. She can stop searching now.

'I… I don't know.' What had Alex said? Say nothing. Stay quiet. Keep your mouth shut. But he didn't take his own advice, in the end. The prospect of death will do that to you. Force you to reassess your life. She certainly had when Alex had got back in touch.

After the initial call, she'd agreed to meet. Alex had sat in front of her, eyes sunken into his head, blank and bleak. 'Please, Meggy,' he'd said. 'This one thing? What else have I got to show for my life, except my time with you guys. Being part of The Five.'

She hadn't been able to take him looking like that, so close to death, when the Alex she'd known had been so vibrant. Fun. Nothing fazed him. Once, when out drinking, he'd known he had gone too far. One shot too many. He was going to be sick. His face had adopted a green pallor, a look that turned to desperation when he knew he wouldn't get to the toilets in time. He'd ducked down under the table with an empty pint glass, made all sorts of awful noises, then emerged, a smile on his face. The pint glass stayed, pushed into a corner, as Alex went straight to the next round.

'Please, Meg,' Alex had said again. There was no youthful exuberance now. 'Call them. Get them to meet me. For one last time.'

She's aware the detectives have been staring at her while she's been sitting, mute, her fingers clenching and unclenching in her lap. She sniffs back tears, then wipes her nose on the edge of her sleeve.

'How can we help you, Meg?' the detective says, his eyes sympathetic.

'I just want everything to go back to the way it was,' she says, quietly.

'And why did everything change?'

But before Meg can reply to the detective's question, there's a loud banging on the door. It opens. A uniformed officer looks apologetic on the threshold.

'I'm sorry, Sarge,' he says. 'But this lady's lawyer is here. Demanded to see her straight away.'

Meg jumps in surprise. The two detectives sit back, arms crossed, clearly annoyed as a man barrels into the room. He's dressed in a smart blue suit, crisp white shirt, navy tie. He brandishes an air of authority like a weapon.

'My client is done here,' he snaps. His voice is loud and decisive. 'Ms Carlton, you're not to say any more. Come with me straight away.'

Can he do this? This strange man she's never seen before. Is he allowed to boss the police around like he's in charge?

'Now,' the man directs.

She looks at the detectives. Butler gives a dismissive gesture, a flap of the hand that says, go on then.

Meg feels an instant swell of relief. She gets up and walks out of the room, following her newly appointed lawyer.

Saved, just in the nick of time.

24

Josh arrives, and Freya's nervous. She looked for him after the interview with Meg Carlton, but hadn't seen him at the nick.

She texted as she arrived home. *Are you coming to mine tonight? x*

He replied. *Yes.*

But what was *that*? No kiss? No comment? She wasn't even sure what time.

But here he is, and he seems the same as normal. A kiss, then a quick, 'Good day?' as he takes his coat off and hangs it next to hers. He starts talking about the cold case he's working on, a dead body found completely decomposed. They need more resources, more time, more officers on the street, but she's not listening.

He stops and looks at her strangely. 'You okay?' he asks. 'You haven't said a word since I arrived. How's your case going? I heard you had one of your suspects in for a voluntary?'

'We did. But just as we were getting something interesting from her, the lawyer turned up and shut it down.'

'That must have pissed Butler off.'

'Yeah.' She stops again. She hasn't got the inclination to talk about the case now; there are bigger things on her mind. She takes a deep breath. 'Josh, what's going on with Elise?'

'Elise?' His face is blank. 'My ex-girlfriend, Elise? Nothing. Why?'

'It's just… After we bumped into her yesterday you were quiet. Why hadn't you told me about the wedding invite?' Freya can't help the bitterness drifting into her tone. Angry for being kept in the dark. 'About your ex-girlfriend getting married?'

Josh stares at her, speechless.

'And your parents. She still speaks to your mum, Josh!'

'They were close,' he says quietly. 'When we were together. They had a lot in common… They…'

'I looked like such an idiot. She must have seen how surprised I was.'

She's standing in front of him, hands on her hips, but now she stops and looks at him. While she's been talking, he's slowly sat down at her kitchen table, his face thoughtful. Oh, shit, there is something going on, she thinks as she lowers herself down next to him. 'Just tell me, Josh, please? I'd rather know.'

He sits silent for a moment. 'Do you want a drink?' he says. He gets up, opens her fridge. 'I want a drink.'

He takes a bottle of wine out of the door and opens it, pouring himself a large glass, then one for her. She takes a sip, then another. He sits down again, pensive.

'So, yes,' he begins. 'I was quiet after seeing Elise. But it's not what you think.'

'What am I thinking?' she says slowly.

'That… I don't know. I love her, or something. That I'm upset about her getting engaged.' Freya feels her face get hot. Exactly what she's been thinking. 'It's not that at all,' he continues. 'Seeing her, there, with you, had the opposite effect, if anything. I was glad I wasn't with her anymore. Those stupid high heels she always wears, the amount of shit she trowels onto her face. Do you know how long it took us to go anywhere? We always had to get taxis because she couldn't walk further than a hundred metres. And we couldn't go out for dinner because of this diet or that diet.' Josh seems to be getting into his stride now, and Freya keeps quiet, letting him talk. She takes another swig from her wine. 'This new bloke, Francesco—'

'Franco.'

'Whatever, I don't care. He seems more her type. "He's in wine." Come on,' Josh says. 'What does that even mean?'

Freya laughs. 'I have no idea.'

'Exactly!' He reaches over, taking her hand. 'Me and you. We make more sense. We can talk about work, and dead bodies and nasty shit, over dinner, and neither of us cares. It's what we do. And that's good for me.'

Freya feels a lovely glow inside. 'So why were you so distant?'

He frowns. He lets go of her hand and interlocks his fingers round the wine glass. 'Promise you won't get upset? Let me talk for a second, let me finish. Because, oh, fuck...' He stops again. The warm, fuzzy feeling has gone; Freya knows this isn't going to be good.

'I was jealous because I want what she's got.'

Freya's confused. 'Franco?'

Josh laughs. 'No! I mean, to get engaged, to get married. To plan a life with someone. And I'd like that to be with you.'

Freya senses a 'but' coming.

'But—' Oh, shit, there it is. 'I feel like there's something missing. With us.'

Freya feels a lump build in her throat. Oh, please, she thinks. I really don't want to break up with you. 'Like what?' she croaks.

'Like you're not telling me something. That there's some aspect of your life I'm not privy to. Something you're holding back on.'

She knows what he's talking about. He means Jonathan.

She's deliberately not told him much about Jon, and how he died. Josh wasn't around then, when Jonathan's murder was investigated by her and Robin. Only Robin knew the awful, career-ending truth: that Freya had withheld the vital information that she was Jonathan Miller's lover, so she could stay on the case. Telling Josh about Jonathan would mean he might realise that horrible lie. And then all manner of secrets – secrets she and Robin have kept hidden for all this time – might come to light.

But he's not stupid. He's a detective, an expert in spotting the holes in someone's story. And now she's going to lose him because of it.

'There's nothing, Josh,' she tries. 'Nothing interesting.'

'What about the man you were seeing before me? I'm sorry to bring it up, because you never talk about him, but you said there was someone else. Someone that died.'

'Yes.' She pauses, her mouth dry. 'Jon.'

'Jon? See, you've never even told me his name before.'

'Why is it important, Josh? He's gone, why does it matter?'

'You wanted to know about Elise, Freya. It's the same thing. I love you.' He reaches out, taking her hands again. He's said it before, but here, now, on the edge of losing him, it's poignant. Freya feels like she's going to cry. 'And

I want to be there for you. Through the good stuff, and the bad.'

'I—' she starts but then stops, tears threatening.

'It's okay.' He shakes his head. 'I don't expect you to tell me now. But it's got to be two-way, this relationship. I promise to share stuff about Elise from now on. Her bloody wedding. Which will be horrible, by the way. Pretentious and overblown and showy.' He points his now empty wine glass at her for emphasis. 'That's why I'm not going, because I don't give a shit about her life anymore. And nor does my mum, for the record. But please, Freya, I need to know. Everything. Don't shut me out. Because if you do, then where can we go?'

Freya nods, weakly. She should be happy. Everything he's saying is positive. He wants to be with her. He wants to live with her, get married one day. He loves her. But a deep ache grows in her stomach. How can she tell him about Jonathan? How can she share how she lied, deceived her boss, her DCI, ultimately ending up complicit in the death of her lover's wife? If he knew, it could mean the end of them.

Josh kisses her lightly on the cheek.

'I'm sorry,' he says with a gentle smile. 'I didn't mean to upset you.'

Freya clears her throat, wiping her eyes quickly. She pulls on a grin, her mouth feeling tight. 'It's fine. I'm sorry, Josh. Give me some time.'

He nods and gets up, heading to the fridge.

They cook together side by side and have dinner. She's not being her usual self but he seems okay with that, letting her think. They put a film on after: guns, explosions, the all-action movie stars barely distracting her away from her thoughts.

She could make something up. Some bullshit story about who Jon was. But he's attuned to finding out lies. She'd make a mistake one day, and he'd spot it and what then? She'd definitely lose him.

She could tell him the truth. But no. No, she thinks. I can't. It's too big a risk.

They clean their teeth. He catches her eye in the mirror as he stands behind her and smiles, his mouth white with toothpaste. They go to bed, turn the light off and slowly, in the dark, they make love. She enjoys the feeling of his body, his hands now familiar with what works, what doesn't. And after, as he curls his body behind hers, entwining their legs, she thinks: what if?

What if she tells him?

What then?

25

Tuesday

Six people sit round the table. Jess Derby, the Crime Scene Manager; Greg Egerton from Digital; a woman from Intel who's been silent so far. Then the detectives: DCI Neal Baker, Robin and Freya. A small case conference, to talk through where they are – and where to go next.

Robin's taking the lead, talking through what they've found out about the case. Freya sits in silence, her head spinning. Still preoccupied by thoughts of Josh after their conversation last night. Robin's talking about the few belongings they found at Alex's office, now bundled up into evidence bags – including his diary and the notepad with her name on it. But what did it show? she wonders, pulling herself back to the case. There was something clearly on his mind, but what?

She flicks through her file, looking for Steph's notes and Alex's medical records.

'He was told he had stage four cancer in July,' she blurts out. Robin stops, mid-sentence; all heads turn to her. 'When he wrote that note.'

'And you think the two events are linked?' Baker asks.

'He thought he was going to die. He started to write a note to a detective. What does that say to you?'

'Or it could have been related to a case with his work. We'll never know,' Robin adds.

Baker sighs. 'Well, from what you've told me so far, Butler, you haven't found any concrete evidence of foul play. The CCTV was clear, right?'

'I went through it last night,' Robin confirms. 'No other parties go in or out between nineteen hundred hours on Christmas Eve and the next morning, when the dog walker arrives just after seven. Supported by Response and Patrol, who have failed to come up with any other eyewitnesses.' He turns to the Crime Scene Manager. 'Jess – how much progress have you made?'

Jess sits up straight and tucks a piece of hair behind her ear. Freya's worked with her before; she's quick, efficient. 'We recovered a number of exhibits from the scene, most significantly the phone belonging to Alex Reynolds, one small silver hip flask, one thermos, two large bottles of spirits and four cans. All with just dregs inside. Alex Reynolds' clothes have been forwarded from the mortuary. We've pulled prints from the bottles and flasks, tapings from his clothes, but without biologicals from the other four there's not much we can do.'

'Did you find the victim's prints anywhere?' Robin asks.

'Yes, on the bottle of whisky and the large thermos. And,' she continues with a smile, 'that's where we found the good stuff.' She pauses for effect. 'Morphine. And a lot of it. Mixed into what we believe was hot chocolate. My guess?' she says, and they all nod. 'The morphine was added to the large thermos, then the others all had some.'

'Knowingly, or otherwise?' Baker asks.

'Can't tell. Although I'd be tempted to say, unwittingly, given the concentrations we found. I had a look at the prescribed drugs you seized from his house, and it was probably the oramorph. Liquid morphine. It tastes sweet, but you wouldn't notice if it was added to something like hot chocolate. Or if your sense of taste was as screwed to hell as Alex Reynolds' would have been.'

'But we have no way of telling if it was added by Alex,' Robin says, 'or someone else.'

'Well,' Jess replies. 'That's where it gets interesting.'

Robin glances to Freya; she can see the excitement on his face. The thrill of a piece of evidence that could shed some light on this whole mess.

'We've printed the oramorph bottle.'

'And?' Robin asks.

'Nothing,' Jess says, and Freya sees Robin's face fall. 'No, no,' Jess continues quickly. 'You're missing my point. We didn't find anything. Not a single print.'

Freya sits up straight in her seat. 'But that's...' she begins.

'Exactly,' Jess says. 'We would have expected to find Alex Reynolds' prints. It was his prescription. The bottle was open – and empty – so we know someone must have handled it.'

Freya looks to Robin. 'Someone wiped it down,' she says. 'But who?'

'That's your job, Detectives,' Jess says with a cheeky grin.

Robin and Freya both look to Baker with anticipation.

'Okay,' their DCI replies. 'It's suspicious, I'll give you that. And now we know how they all ended up in that state. And how Alex Reynolds died. The how, but not the who or the why.'

'Or even if an actual crime has been committed,' Freya adds, slightly deflated. 'The wiped bottle just shows someone didn't want their prints on there, not that they added it to the flask. Were there any others found?'

'There was a real mix on the thermos,' Jess replies. 'It's a perfect surface for prints, lovely and shiny, and it was covered. We managed to untangle Reynolds', but there are definitely some others. Get me their samples and I'll compare.' She smiles, happily. 'A thousand-piece jigsaw with no picture on the box.'

'We have Meg Carlton's now,' Freya says. 'Can you check for hers first?'

'I'll get on it.'

'So what are your theories?' Baker interjects. 'Following this line of thought, who put the morphine in there?'

'Sara Williams is a GP,' Freya suggests. 'Maybe she got hold of some?'

'But it's a controlled substance,' Robin counters. 'They don't just have it lying around in a surgery.'

Freya nods. 'So let's assume Alex Reynolds was the only person with access. Maybe he put some in his own drink, maybe he got the dose wrong... Deliberately or otherwise.'

'Suicide?' Baker asks.

'Nobody that knows him thinks so. Emphatically not, in fact.'

'And you've ruled out an act of revenge? From one of his clients.'

'I think it's unlikely,' Robin replies. 'There were no reported incidents on the PNC or the RMS. Plus, it's a weird way to go about it. It wasn't a beating on a street corner. It was a remote beach, on Christmas Eve.'

'Agreed,' Baker confirms.

'And suicide wouldn't explain their strange behaviour,' Robin continues, with a frown. 'Why hadn't they spoken in twenty years? As confirmed by Meg Carlton,' he adds, for Baker's benefit. 'Why get back in touch after all this time?'

'Maybe they were the only people he had.' The quiet woman from Intel speaks for the first time. She flushes as all eyes turn to her; she looks furiously at the table. 'Victoria Welsh, guv. I looked into all five of them, as you asked. And it didn't take long.' She passes out reports, paper fluttering. Freya takes hers and flicks through. 'No criminal records,' she continues. 'Not even a speeding ticket. Nothing contentious on social media. In fact, Sam Bowen has no accounts at all. Not even Facebook.'

'That's unusual in itself,' Robin comments. Freya knows even Robin's on Facebook, and he can't stand that social stuff. 'Did you find out where they used to live?'

Welsh nods. 'Twenty-eight Shakespeare Avenue, Portswood. For two years, from July 1998 until the end of June 2000.'

'Most people live in halls for their first year of uni at Southampton,' Freya explains.

Victoria carries on: 'Personal info: Carlton and Reynolds are single. Registry office shows Sara Gold and Mike Williams marrying in November 2000.'

'Just after graduating uni,' Robin comments to Freya. 'They hadn't been together long.'

Freya turns to Victoria. 'How old are their kids?'

'Freddy Williams, age eleven. Tabitha Williams – thirteen.'

'So it wasn't that,' Freya says. 'Unless she was pregnant and miscarried?'

'Maybe. Not sure how it helps us, though,' Robin replies. He looks back to Victoria and gives a gesture to say, carry on.

Victoria turns back to her notes. 'Sara Williams is the only one with a social life, and that seems limited to her mummy friends,' she says, putting the last two words in inverted commas either side of her head.

'And Sam Bowen?'

'He's the exception. Divorced twice, as you know. One daughter, not with either of his ex-wives – another woman. It doesn't look like he sees her much, although regular payments go out to the mother. A lot of work conferences. Official photos of him, drinks in hand, women on his arm.'

'So, no massive red flags on any of them?' Baker comments.

'No.'

'Any evidence of an affair with Sara Williams?' Freya asks.

'Not that I can see. But I'll keep digging.'

'Please,' Baker says. He turns to Freya and Robin. 'Have you thought about interviewing them again? Properly? Drag them all in here for a voluntary, threaten them with arrest and see how far they go?'

Robin looks to Freya. 'West? What do you think?'

'Meg Carlton was our best bet, guv,' she replies to Baker. 'But she lawyered up. I think the others will do the same. Let's get something concrete we can throw in their faces and go from there.'

Robin nods in approval.

'Fine,' Baker agrees. 'Greg, you keep going on that mobile phone. Jess – the fingerprints from the thermos the first moment you can. Let us know about any matches for Meg Carlton. And you two—' He turns to Robin and Freya. 'Do as you said, keep digging. The fact this lot are refusing to share any sort of useful information pisses me off enough to continue. A man is dead. Mike Williams might lose his fingers. That's potentially murder. GBH at least. If it was deliberate or any of this lot had a hand in his death, I want one of these fuckers charged. If not all.'

Nods from everyone. 'Yes, guv.'

'Agreed,' Baker says. He puts his meaty hands on the table and pushes himself to his feet. 'Let me know when you find something.'

26

Baker departs; Greg skulks off towards the canteen. Jess and Victoria gather their piles of paper and leave Freya and Robin in the conference room.

'What about us?' Freya asks.

'You went to Southampton Uni, didn't you?' Robin says.

'Yes,' she confirms. 'But a few years after these guys. I graduated in 2006.'

She looks up. Robin has a grin on his face. 'Do you want to give me a tour of the area?'

–

They get into Robin's car and drive away from Central Southampton towards Portswood. They head through Highfield, past the university, where new shiny glass buildings tower over the old run-down houses that stood in Freya's day. There is a new swimming pool, but the student union looks the same; Hartley Library is unchanged.

'What was it like?' Robin asked. 'Going to uni here?'

'Fun. Nice, I mean.' She shrugs. 'I can't compare it to anywhere else, but I liked it.'

'Were you part of any clubs?'

'Only the law society.'

'Shit, I forgot you have a degree in law.'

She smiles. 'How differently life could have worked out for me, huh? Could have been wearing pinstriped suits and spike heels, making six figures. Instead, I'm stuck with you.' His brief snort of laughter is his only response. She points towards the small pub on the corner. The Dog and Duck. 'That's where Sara Williams used to work.'

'Interesting,' he says quietly.

Some things have changed in the small suburb of Portswood – the new Sainsbury's, the two gawdy ice-cream parlours – but others have stayed reassuringly unaffected by time. The Mitre on the corner, Portswood Hardware, Charcoal Grill, the Gordon Arms. The high street is busy; the world is coming back to life after the lull of Christmas. They turn right at the lights and pull into what used to be Safeway, now taken over by Waitrose.

The car park is full of shoppers, keen to stock up on essentials. Freya thinks of her own fridge: empty and neglected, as it often is when she gets caught up in a new case. Robin has stopped, his car keys in hand, looking to his right. She follows his gaze to the far side of the car park – a smaller walled area, trees pushing over the bricks. The concrete has been dug up, piles of core and earth to one side, a small red digger *in situ*.

'What happened there?' he asks.

'They were doing some resurfacing work and found a body,' she says. The unmistakable blue-and-white police tape has been strung up between the wall and the digger. *Police Line Do Not Cross*. Some of it has fallen down; it flaps silently in the breeze. 'That's the cold case Josh has been seconded to.'

Robin squints at the police tape. 'How cold?' he asks.

She shrugs. 'Cold enough that they haven't been able to get an ID. Any more than that, I don't know.' He nods slowly, and they start to walk away. For the first time, she makes the connection as Robin has: a body found in the very town where these people lived as students. Around the same time that one of them dies. 'I'll call Josh later, find out more about it.'

'Good idea,' Robin says as they walk.

He follows her down one of the side streets. She's already looked up the address, recognising familiar road names from her time here all those years ago. She points off to their left.

'I lived down there. Tennyson Road. Number sixty-nine.' Robin gives her a look. 'I know, I know,' she says with a grin. 'Unfortunate. Five girls in one house. Place was a shithole. Here.'

They've arrived at the start of Shakespeare Avenue. It's a long road, quiet, away from the noise of the high street. Cars line up bumper to bumper down both sides. Old, smaller vehicles: a Peugeot 206, Nissan Micra, VW Polo. Some remain undisturbed after the freezing weather, ice forming in hard blocks across the windscreens. Others have been scraped in messy lines.

The houses are similar – big bay windows running across two floors, small concrete front yards where wheelie bins and plastic crates of empty glass bottles reside. They start to walk down the road. Paint peels from windowsills, music drifts from open windows; there's the smell of burgers and fried food in the air. A younger man with bare legs, slippers and a dirty dressing gown steps out of his front door and drops something in the bin; he regards Freya and Robin with suspicion.

Freya counts down the houses. Then there it is: number twenty-eight, the former residence of 'The Five'. She forms inverted commas round the words in her head. Friends so close they had their own nickname. But estranged, so they didn't even go to the wedding of two of them barely six months after? Freya can't make sense of it. She knows she's grown apart from her own university friends over the years, distance and time getting in the way, but the instant split doesn't seem natural.

She looks up at the house. It has a large bay window and a white-painted front door with a small, tiled step. A row of candles are lined up along the windowsill, a dream-catcher is suspended above. It seems like a dangerous combination to Freya.

'Should we knock?' Robin asks.

'A student house, the week after Christmas? Nobody's going to be in.'

He presses the doorbell. They hear it echo through the house but as she predicted, there's no answer.

'Worth a try,' Robin says, taking a step back from the front door. Then he smiles. 'Do you fancy a drink?'

27

The Dog and Duck isn't big. Former employer of Sara Williams and the source of new-found curiosity for Robin. The pub sits on the corner of the street, in between a kebab shop and a row of houses.

'Who'd want to live there?' Robin asks in a half-whisper.

'Students?'

'Course.'

It's nearly midday, a respectable hour for a pint. Robin wants to think; to sit and discuss all of this with Freya. Theories run round in his head, all conflicting. It feels like he's missing something, a thread that will pull it together.

He pushes the handle down and opens the door into the bar. Freya follows. He expected a locals' pub but inside the decor is new and clean, no lingering odour of old beer and dirty carpets. They walk up to the bar; he spots a pile of board games on the right-hand side, a dartboard to the left. Through an open door, there's the tantalising edge of a pool table.

The place is quiet; a few punters sit nursing their pints at darkened tables. Robin assumes it will be different in term time, with students frequenting the pub all hours of the day.

'What can I get you?' the woman asks when they're next to the bar.

Robin runs his gaze over the offerings on tap. 'A half of Forty-Niner,' he says. 'Frey?'

She sighs. 'You're a bad influence,' she complains ineffectually. 'A white wine. Small,' she adds quickly.

They carry their drinks to a table on the far side and sit down. The wood is worn, but it's clean and varnished, the beer mat new.

'Robin, what are we doing here?' Freya whispers.

'Getting a feel for the home town of our suspects.'

'By drinking on duty?'

'I figured you need it.' He's noticed the black rings under her eyes; the way she's moving, slow and worn out. She's been uncharacteristically quiet all morning. 'What happened last night? With Josh?'

She looks up quickly. Robin notices a flash of guilt, before she lowers her eyes again to her glass. 'Not much,' she says. 'We talked. It was fine.'

'He's not in love with his ex?'

'No. But...' She shakes her head. 'It doesn't matter.'

Robin frowns. He's no good with personal stuff, especially where women are concerned. He makes a mental note to speak to Mina when they get back to the nick, see if she can take Freya off for a coffee and a chat.

He takes a sip of his beer and considers the case. They all went to university here, spent their time in this little town, Sara Williams working in this very pub.

'What are we missing, Freya?' Robin asks. She looks up, listening. 'These five were close, spent every day together. Then they don't talk for twenty years until Alex Reynolds finds out he's going to die, and he contacts them out of nowhere.'

'Making amends for something?' Freya says. The expression on her face is unusually solemn.

He looks at her for a second. What on earth is going on in her head today? 'Maybe,' he replies. 'But what?' He points to the woman behind the bar. 'How long do you think she's worked here?'

Freya follows his gaze. 'Decades,' she says, a hint of a smile catching her eyes.

Robin stands up and Freya follows him to the bar. The woman looks over with curiosity as he gets his warrant card out.

'DS Robin Butler,' he says. 'DC Freya West.'

Her face changes instantly. While before she looked slightly sleepy, bored of waiting for punters to serve, she's suddenly alert. Her eyes are wide, body poised.

'Is it him?' she says.

Robin pauses. 'Him, who?'

'The body you found, in the car park. Is it him? My father?'

Robin glances to Freya, who looks as confused as he is. 'I'm sorry, we were here on another matter. But can you tell me what you're talking about?'

A flash of anger passes over the woman's face. 'I was away. When you found it. The body. So I missed all the press appeals at the beginning. But when I got back and saw the police tape, I knew.'

'And you think it's your father?' Freya asks.

'Yes. Kevin Gillis. That's his name. I called the hotline as soon as I got back, on Christmas Eve, but no one's returned my call. I thought… I thought…' Her body caves in on itself slightly. 'When you said you were detectives, I thought you were coming here to confirm. That it was him. And he's dead.'

Robin nods slowly. 'Thank you. Mrs…'

'Miss. Gillis. Beth Gillis. I own this place. Took it over from my father.'

'If you'd like to bear with us for a second, we'll make some calls.'

Robin moves away to the back of the pub, Freya following.

'You don't think…' Freya starts.

'I do. Call Josh.'

Freya dials; Josh answers straight away.

'What's up, babe?'

Babe? Robin thinks. But now is not the time for a piss-take.

'Josh, you're on speaker. Robin and I… We're at a pub in Portswood. And the owner thinks your cold case is her father. She says she left a message on the tipline.' There's a long pause. 'Josh?'

'No one's checked that since Christmas,' he says at last. 'What's her name? Her father's name?'

'Kevin Gillis,' Robin replies. 'When did this body turn up?'

'Beginning of December,' Josh says. 'Wait a sec. I'm checking our misper list.'

'And it's a man?'

'Yeah. Been dead a while, so Dr Harper couldn't confirm exact TOD. At least fifteen years, she said. Ah. Here. Yes, he's here.' Another pause, the line crackling. 'He was one of our possibilities. But we called his next of kin, couldn't get hold of her.'

'Well, she's here now. We'll get some details, phone you back.'

They end the call and turn; Beth Gillis is watching them. She sees the expression on their faces and her hand flies to her mouth.

'It's him,' she repeats once they're closer.

'It could be,' Robin says. 'We'll need a DNA sample from you for comparison.' She nods. 'When did he go missing?'

'Um...' She starts to talk but her voice catches. Freya puts a hand out, sympathetically touching her arm.

'Take your time.'

The woman nods, eyes growing wet with tears. 'June,' she says. 'June 2000.'

Freya glances to Robin.

'You're sure?' he asks.

'Certain. You never forget the date your father disappeared.'

Robin feels Freya's gaze and he turns, meeting her eyes. He knows what she's thinking.

Alex Reynolds was a man nobody believes would kill himself, despite his terminal illness. He gathers his friends from university back together, and hours later he is dead.

Kevin Gillis, Sara Williams' former boss, goes missing in June 2000. The exact month the residents of 28 Shakespeare Avenue stop talking to each other.

There's something strange going on. There's no way this is coincidence. Alex Reynolds died because of something that happened at the end of their time at university.

And Robin's going to prove it.

Part 2

28

Sara sits in her empty house. The cup of tea is long cold in front of her; her hands rest by her side. She is still, her eyes closed: a perfect picture of calm. Inside she is anything but.

She is alone. With the kids staying away, with Mike gone, the house is silent. And the control she has carefully cultivated is crumbling. Her body remembers what it is like not to feel safe. She is purposeless, unable to concentrate, wandering the empty rooms, checking the windows, the locks on the door. She hasn't slept. When she tries, the nightmares come. Flickering images. A fear that starts in her stomach, that catches her breath, leaving her choking and unable to cry out in the dark.

Awake, her body exists in a state of hypervigilance. Listening for the slightest sound. Waiting for the glimpse of *something* that will send her back.

She debates calling him. A million times she picks up her phone, but what can he do? He couldn't help her then, he can't now.

She'd wanted retribution. She'd wanted revenge. But not this.

Never this.

29

'Tell us what you know.'

The four of them sit round a table in the incident room: Freya and Robin on one side, Josh and Mina on the other. They're there to talk about the dead body under the car park, Robin convening a meeting as soon as they got back from Portswood.

'I don't know much, I've only just been seconded,' Josh begins. 'Mouse—'

'DI Ratcliffe to you,' Robin snaps.

Josh turns red, scalded by Robin's tone.

'DI Ratcliffe is in charge and he's off for the holidays,' Josh concludes quietly.

'I can help,' Mina says, and Freya breathes a sigh of relief. Everyone calls DI Ratcliffe Mouse. Everyone. But it looks like Robin's in a bad mood and Josh is his punching bag.

'The body was found by workmen on the sixth of December,' Mina says, calmly. The file is in front of her, but she isn't looking at it. Like all of her cases, Mina knows the details off by heart. 'Work on the car park had been scheduled for months. The tarmac had been splitting, and they believed it was down to subsidence so the whole lot needed to come out. They'd barely got started before the digger hit the body. It was under the top layer of concrete, a metre down.'

'And it's definitely a man?' Freya asks. She glances at Robin; his eyebrows are low, focused on Mina as she talks.

'Definitely. Dr Harper confirmed. And it's been down there some time.'

'But you'd not been able to get an ID?'

'No. We've put out appeals to the public, gone through the misper database, but it's Christmas. People are slow to come back, distracted by other things. And Steph couldn't be too accurate with the timeline, so there are a number of possibles.' Mina pauses. 'You're thinking it's Kevin Gillis? The father of your bar owner? And it's related to your incident on Christmas Eve?'

Robin stands up. 'Yes,' he replies, quickly. 'Freya, have a read of the file. Keep me informed.'

He leaves and Mina widens her eyes at Freya in disbelief. 'What's got into him?'

'He's pissed off he missed it.' She looks at Josh, who's silent next to her. 'Don't take it personally, Josh.'

'Yeah, well,' he snaps back. 'Hard not to when he's been like that for months.' He gets up. 'I need coffee,' he grumbles and heads off.

'Wow, all the boys are in a mood today,' Mina comments, sitting back in her seat. She gives Freya a sympathetic look. 'How are things between the two of you?'

'Okay. Better,' Freya replies. Although she's not feeling that right now. Ever since their argument last night, things have been strained. The thought of telling Josh about Jonathan plays on her mind. She needs to talk to Robin. But now is definitely not the time.

She thinks back to the interview with the owner of the Dog and Duck, Beth Gillis. Her shoulders slumped as she stood behind the bar. Then she turned, took a glass and filled it from one of the optics behind her. She paused, waited for it to top up, then took another shot, as Robin and Freya stared.

'Do you want one?' she asked, and Freya hastily shook her head.

'Would you like to come and sit down,' Robin said instead, pointing to a table.

The three of them sat in a circle, Beth Gillis taking quick sips of the brown liquid. Then she started to cry, her head folding into her chest, her arms covering her face. They sat, mute, while she sobbed. Freya put a hand on her arm.

The woman looked at it. Then she wiped her eyes, slowly. 'How long until you'll know for sure?' she asked, her voice wet with grief.

'As soon as we can. We'll put a rush on it,' Robin said.

She nodded. 'Thank you. I don't know why I'm so upset. I knew. I knew he was dead. I had him declared, you know. About ten years after he disappeared.' Robin handed her a tissue, while Freya watched her closely. She seemed genuinely upset. Shocked by the news of her father's death.

Beth looked up. 'I had to. For the pub. I was running it without him, but it got so difficult to do things. Changing the terms of the lease, all that legal stuff, with his name on the property.' For the first time a flash of guilt passed across her face. 'It was much easier once I owned this place. You think that's awful, don't you?'

'No, not at all,' Freya replied softly. 'You did what you had to do.'

'Could we ask you about the pub at that time?' Robin said. 'About the staff?'

'Sure, but I won't be able to tell you much. After Dad disappeared, we had to close for a few months. I hadn't been involved with the pub before – I was away, living in another part of the country. And when I reopened it, I employed a completely different set of people.'

'So the name Sara Gold doesn't mean anything to you?'

She shook her head.

'Alex Reynolds? Sam Bowen, Mike Williams, Meg Carlton?'

'No. I'm sorry. I could go through the old records if that would help? But it would only show the basics. You know – pay, employment dates. That sort of thing.'

'That would be helpful, thank you. Can you tell us what happened around the time of his disappearance?'

She nodded, wiping her eyes again and finishing her whisky, composing herself. 'We used to speak every weekend, usually Sunday night. He'd tell me about the customers, his regulars. They'd become his friends. It wasn't until I got hold of the accounts that I realised how little money the pub actually made.'

'It wasn't a student bar in those days?' Robin asked.

'Definitely not. An old man's pub, through and through. When I took it over, I gave it a bit of a makeover. Ran student nights, you know. Promotions. Anything to get people in the door. It's only over the last few years it's started to make a profit.' She smiled weakly. 'So you can't say I killed him for the money.'

Robin smiled back. 'And what happened the week he went missing?' he prompted.

'He didn't call. I wasn't worried straight away. He was often late. But then one of his employees phoned. Said the bar had been closed for a few days. I drove down, expecting him ill in bed in the flat above, but the place was locked up tight.'

'And you reported him missing that day?'

'I knew something had happened. It was so unlike him to go anywhere. And there was the thing with the floor.'

'The floor?'

'Yeah, in the kitchen, behind the bar. It had this grubby lino, but the whole thing had been ripped up. Nothing but dirty tiles underneath.'

That got their attention. 'Can we come in? Get a scene of crime team to take a look?'

Her eyes turned cold. 'You want to look now? Twenty years later? The police dismissed it. They said there was nothing they could do. That he'd probably gone off somewhere, alone, and he'd call.'

'I'm sorry about that,' Robin said. 'But those were different times. And it's possible we can still find a trace of something.'

She nodded slowly. 'Do what you like. I don't care. I'll sell this place now. I was at a loose end when he disappeared. Just out of uni, no job, didn't want to see it go to a stranger. That's why I took it over. But I can't bear the thought of it. That he might have been killed here.' She looked down to the tabletop, fingers twisting round each other. 'He'd been out there all along, hadn't he?' she said, directing her question to Freya. 'Around the corner, under the concrete.'

Freya nodded. 'I'm sorry for your loss,' she murmured. Because when there were no excuses, there was nothing else to say.

–

She repeats the story to Mina, her friend's face softening.

'Poor woman,' Mina agrees. 'But how is her dead father linked to your guys?'

Freya sighs and sits back in her seat. Her hands cradle her now cold mug of tea. 'I don't know, Mina. But don't you think it's odd that the same time he went missing, this lot all stopped talking to each other? And they only get back together once the body is found? Plus, he owned the pub where Sara Williams worked.'

'I get that. But it's a bit of a stretch to assume they killed him.'

'I know. And we don't even have anything definite to show that Alex's death on Christmas Eve was deliberate, let alone any link to this guy.'

Freya looks through the meeting room window to the office, where Robin has sat down at his desk, a scowl still on his face. Mina follows her gaze.

'I thought I came to work to get away from the childish squabbling,' Mina comments with a grin.

'Seems that some kids never grow out of it,' Freya replies. She watches as Greg comes into the room, heading towards Robin. 'I better go,' she says quickly to Mina, keen to be included in whatever he's found.

Greg smiles when he sees Freya.

'Internet search results,' he says. 'From Reynolds' phone.'

He hands it to Robin, despite the fact she's closest, making Freya's teeth grate with annoyance.

Robin looks at it, then hands it to Freya. 'That confirms it then,' he says, softly.

She looks at the printed sheet. It contains a number of lines of text. Some banal and boring, remnants of his social life, or snippets about actors or programmes that Alex was watching on TV. But the one that Greg has highlighted speaks volumes.

body found police portswood

A few words typed into the search engine, then the web pages Google had directed him to. One from the *Hampshire Chronicle*, detailing the initial discovery as the builders made their grisly find. And one, later, as DI Ratcliffe and his team appealed for information.

'The dates tally with the initial emails,' Greg adds.

Freya looks at Robin. 'So he saw this, knew the body had been found, and started emailing his mates?'

'Hardly subtle,' Robin mutters. 'Thanks, Greg. Anything else on the phone?'

'Nothing else to report. But shout if you need me,' he says, and ambles off across the office.

Robin looks up to Freya. 'Sorry,' he says. 'For the bad mood in there.'

'It's not me you need to apologise to,' she comments with a nod towards Josh. He's sat, his back hunched, doing something on his computer. Robin frowns, a thought that clearly disagrees with him.

'Do you want a coffee?' he says instead.

'Go on then.'

She follows him to the kitchen, keen to continue their discussion about the case. 'So how do we prove all this?' she asks. 'It was twenty years ago.'

Robin clicks the kettle on and picks his mug out of the sink, then another for her.

'Assuming they did kill him,' Robin comments, as Freya takes the milk out of the fridge. She sniffs it and winces. It's obviously still not been replaced since

Christmas. She pours it down the sink, dropping the plastic container in the bin. 'What motive could they possibly have for killing a pub landlord?'

'A money angle? Sara Williams was stealing from the pub and he found out.' Robin gives her a look. 'I know, I know. It's weak,' she concedes.

He dries the mugs and spoons instant coffee in. Freya notes he's using Little Miss Sunshine as normal, and wonders where her present to him has gone. 'Can you call Jess?' he says. 'Get SOCO into the Dog and Duck as soon as possible. And I'll get the sample from Beth Gillis off to the lab to compare to the dead body. I'm seeing Steph tonight. Get some insight into what she found on Kevin Gillis.'

'Insight? Is that what you call it now?' Freya remarks with a grin. Her boss's history with the forensic pathologist is well known to her, a coupling she's always approved of.

'Not like that,' he replies. She continues to stare at him, smiling. 'It is possible to be friends, you know,' he comments, then hands her the coffee. 'Go and do some work. Bloody women,' he mutters as he heads back to his desk. 'Always trying to set me up.'

She watches him go, taking his coffee with him. She notices the mug again, feeling a slight stirring of worry. Had she pissed him off in some way? Been insensitive in highlighting everything he's been through? Maybe it would have been better if she'd left it alone; he hadn't bought her anything for Christmas – or her birthday. Or anything, ever, for that matter.

And if she has annoyed him, it's only going to get worse. Things between her and Josh have been weird. Almost forced. He's making out that everything is normal, but every now and again she catches him looking at her strangely. As if he's deciding whether to ask her directly about Jonathan.

She knows he's right. She can understand how he's feeling: the fact Josh left her in the dark over Elise's wedding still rankles. And she wants to tell him. A few times she's opened her mouth to start talking but silenced herself immediately. She tells Josh who Jonathan was, and what happened, and there's a chance it will all be over. He'll be horrified at her breaking the rules and investigating his murder; he might even report her, and then what? She'll lose her job and her boyfriend. But isn't it worth the risk? the little voice in her head squeaks. He might appreciate her honesty and they'll be able to move forward. Get a place together? Get married? Even – and she barely dares to think it – have children?

But first, she needs to speak to Robin. As soon as she tells Josh, the first question he'll ask is, 'Did Butler know?' She needs to make sure he's on side. Get their stories straight.

Like the common criminals they are.

30

It's nice to be back here, Robin thinks, as he stands at the bar waiting for his pint of Doom Bar to be pulled. The low bubble of conversation, nice calm music – not too loud. Squishy brown leather sofas, perfect for his weary body at the end of a long day.

'Sorry I'm late, have you been here long?' Steph appears at his side; she reaches up and plants a kiss on his cheek.

'No, not at all,' he says with a smile. 'G and T?'

'Please. Large.'

He orders from the barman, who places a goldfish-bowl-sized drink in front of Steph. Freya's words from earlier play on his mind.

'Let's go out for dinner,' Steph had said when he'd suggested a chat about the case. 'I can't live my whole life in that mortuary.'

'Are you driving?' he asks her now, as she takes a long sip from her drink.

'Dumped my car at home. Fancied a few.'

Interesting.

They carry their drinks to a table, picking up a menu on the way. They sit down opposite each other. It's the first time they've been here in a while, and for a moment they sit in silence, staring at their menus.

'How have you been, Robin?'

'Good. You?'

'Same.' Silence again.

They talk about food – steak and chips for him, veggie lasagne for her – then order more drinks.

'So, the PM?' Steph asks.

Robin is relieved. Easy ground, something to take away the awkwardness. 'Were there any useful findings?'

'Well.' She pulls a file out of her bag and opens it on the table between them. Full-colour photographs of old grey bones stare out. 'As you can see, there wasn't much left. The concrete protected him from above, but all the usual creepy-crawlies did their work from below.'

'How long do you think he'd been in the ground?'

'The speed of skeletonisation of a buried cadaver depends on a number of factors, but broadly speaking soft tissues will be absent after two years. Tendons, ligaments, hair and nails go after that, so after about five years bones will be bare and disarticulated. However,' she says, tapping a finger on the photo, 'we were well past that.'

'Can you date the bones?' Robin asks.

'Possibly. We'd have to get an anthropologist or an archaeologist involved. Personally, I think your best bet lies with your own Major Crimes team.'

Robin knows that Smith and Mina are hard at work trying to find out when the concrete was laid. They know that, then that's the shortest time the body was interred.

'And cause of death? Did you find anything suspicious?'

'Apart from the fact he was a metre under concrete?' Steph smiles.

'Yes, apart from that.'

'Let me start by telling you what we do know. There was no evidence of blunt force trauma. No fractures or breaks in the bones close to time of death. There is an old heal from a broken tibia, which would correspond to the medical records of your missing man, Kevin Gillis, and age and height would also tally.'

'So you think it could be him?'

'DNA comparison to his daughter is pending, but likely, yes. We have no organs, skin, blood vessels, or anything that could help us rule out natural causes, such as heart attack or stroke.'

The waiter comes over with their food, distracting them for a second. He gives a long look to the graphic photos and Steph moves them away with an apologetic grimace. Questions about ketchup or sauces are asked and answered, a new drinks order taken.

Robin picks up his steak knife and makes a cut. He tries not to make the analogy between his meal and what Steph gets up to on her mortuary table. 'So, any idea about COD?'

'Well…' Steph opens the file again and takes out one photo. It shows two curved bones, side by side on the table. 'Do you know what these are?'

'Ribs?'

'Correct. And do you see here?' She points to two tiny nicks on the bone. 'Two grooves, side by side. The placement of the fourth and fifth ribs, directly over the heart, and the location of these furrows would indicate a sharp implement being inserted with some force into the body, through the thoracic wall, probably hitting the heart. If that was the case, he would have bled out quickly, possibly within minutes.'

'So there would have been a crime scene with a lot of blood.'

'Exactly. You know about the lino, right?'

He nods. He's been through the file that afternoon, read about the large sheet of lino the body had been enclosed in. Another solid indicator that it's the man from the pub.

'It's down with the lab now. They might get something off it, you never know. Although after all this time, any biologicals have probably degraded.'

'Any idea about the size of the knife?' Robin asks.

'I'll make some estimates. And I know the lab are working through the soil and other debris found around the body. They might get something from that. Now,' she says with a smile. 'Can we talk about something else? It's been too long, Butler. I need a proper update.'

–

Talk about him is brief, as there's little to discuss. Not much in his life has changed, bar his new ability to run a 10K. Steph manages to look impressed, despite her own proficiency in knocking out triathlons with much less effort. They laugh at his recent attempts at internet dating; she keeps quiet about any of her own. They finish dinner, share a dessert and just before they're about to order coffee, Robin realises that he is really quite drunk. But in a good way. Any of his usual morose tendencies have vanished; he feels relaxed. Almost happy.

They both decline drinks; Robin pays the bill.

'No, I insist,' he says when she protests. 'You're using your spare time to talk dead people.'

She laughs. 'My favourite topic of conversation.'

They get up, walk to the door. She staggers slightly and he catches her. She leaves his arm on hers as they walk out to the street, looking for taxis.

He likes the feeling of her weight, light on his arm. Next to him. A taxi appears in the distance, light glowing yellow in the darkness, and he feels a pang of disappointment as she waves it down. It pulls up next to them.

'So,' he starts. 'You'll call me? If you find anything else.'

'Of course,' she replies. She opens the car door, then stands on her tiptoes and he leans down. But to his surprise, instead of pecking him on the cheek, she puts her gloved hands either side of his face and pulls him round to look at her. She smiles, then kisses him.

'Come on,' the taxi driver hollers. 'You're letting the heat out. Where to?'

'Mine,' Steph replies, without taking her eyes off Robin. 'Are you coming?'

Robin gets in.

–

They kiss in the taxi. A full-blown snog, there's no subtlety here. The alcohol and the rekindling of their old spark obliterate any hesitation in either of them. More kissing in her doorway, more as they go up the stairs, laughing, discarding clothes as they go.

He missed this; he missed her. Why didn't it work last time? he thinks as he kisses her neck, his mouth working downward. They were good together; they *are* good, he thinks as he gasps, her hands doing things that she needs to stop doing *now*, otherwise it's all going to be over very, very quickly.

And after, when he has managed to hold on just long enough to make it a decent shag, he remembers. She wanted children, he didn't. But that's all okay now. After the events of the last year, he has managed to work out a few things in his head, and he's concluded that actually, yes, a family would be pretty great.

'Tell me more about some of those dates,' Steph says. She's lying on her side, her head on the pillow, hair splayed out behind her. He mirrors her posture, facing her.

'What's there to tell? They were all awful.'

'Nobody special then?'

'Absolutely not.'

'Who was the worst? Wait a sec, wait a sec. I'm desperate for a wee. Hold that thought.'

She gets up, naked, and dashes to the bathroom. He rolls over onto his back and sighs, contentedly. The alcohol is fading but not enough for any hangover to kick in. He could definitely get used to this.

The curtains are open a fraction, light shining in from outside, so he gets up quickly to close them. And then he sees it. On the windowsill, in a small brown pot, is the shell he gave her at the beach barely a few days ago. A whelk, pink and delicate. She'd kept it, but why?

He hears the chain flush and puts it down again quickly, jumping back into bed and pulling the duvet across.

She climbs in next to him.

'You were saying?'

He sighs. 'Okay, fine. The worst one – she must have been about twenty-five. No more than that.'

'Robin! You're, what? Forty?'

'Forty-three.'

'That's terrible.' She feigns shock and he laughs.

'I know. But she seemed keen. And I assumed that she'd meet me and we'd have maybe one drink and she'd make her excuses. That would be it. But she didn't. If anything, she was even more enthusiastic when it was time to go.'

He'd found it odd, even then. That this gorgeous, much younger, woman was interested in him. But his ego was flattered. And when she'd invited him back to hers, he'd said yes.

'You dirty old man.'

'I know,' he says again. He pauses.

She senses his reluctance and smiles slowly. 'Go on, then. What happened?'

'I'm not sure I want to tell you this.'

'You have to now. The more embarrassing, the better. Could you not get it up?'

'No, it wasn't that.'

'What then?'

He hesitates. 'She wanted to call me Daddy.'

'No!' Steph roars with laughter. Then she stops. 'And did she?'

'Yes. No. Kind of. It was excruciating.' Steph laughs again. 'I couldn't go through with it. Got out of there as quickly as possible.'

'Oh god, that poor girl. Who knows what horrible issues she has mouldering away in there.'

'I know. Oh, fuck.' Robin puts his hands over his face. 'I can't believe I told you that. What about you?' He turns towards her. 'Come on, Steph. Share. You can't tell me I'm the only person you've been out with in the last year.'

The expression on her face changes. The laughter fades. 'No. Not at all.' She reaches over and takes his hand in hers. 'Listen, Robin. We can't do this again.'

He hesitates, not understanding. 'This?'

'Us. Together.'

'Okay...'

'It's just...' She entwines her fingers through his, staring at their hands. 'I met someone and... it might have a chance to go somewhere.'

He looks at her until she shifts her gaze, her brown eyes meeting his.

'*We* might go somewhere,' he says quietly. 'What I said back then... You know, about not wanting kids. Things have changed.'

'Oh, Robin...' Steph says sadly. 'I'm sorry.'

She doesn't add anymore, but Robin knows. You had your chance, and you blew it. He's not angry with her for sleeping with him, even though she knew that it would go no further. After all, that was what their relationship was based on at the start. Friends with benefits – and then, it had been fine. But something's changed.

'Do you want me to go?' he asks.

'No. No, stay,' she whispers. 'I'm not kicking you out.' She settles back on the pillow, closing her eyes. Their hands still touching.

She's found someone who makes her happy, and for that he's pleased. He just wishes it hadn't left him feeling so empty. So hollow inside.

31

Wednesday

Beth Gillis stands in her pub, her eyes downcast, her hand gently resting over her mouth. Robin watches her as she talks to Freya. He's searching for any signs of guilt, or hesitation, or worry, but she just looks like a woman grieving. A woman who has finally had confirmation that her missing father is dead.

The results came through that morning: the DNA of the dead man was a paternal match to Beth. A chance of over 99 per cent that he was her father. Robin offered the news apologetically as they arrived that morning, SOCO teams in tow, and she nodded, silent.

Now, the white suits have taken over the kitchen. Robin walks over to Freya; she is showing Beth a photograph of the lino. The lino the body was wrapped in when it was buried, covered in blood and mud. It's not a nice sight, and Robin braces himself for a reaction as she looks at it.

But she nods calmly. 'Yes,' she says. 'That was it. See, here.'

The three of them walk behind the bar, and Beth opens a wooden door, revealing the inside of a cupboard where the old flooring remains.

'When we redid it, I couldn't be bothered to clear out properly,' she explains. Robin crouches down and looks at it. It's clean, unfaded, but definitely the same pattern.

'We'll need this, too, if that's okay,' he says.

'Sure.'

The door rattles, distracting them.

'We're closed,' Beth shouts. 'Can't you bloody read?' she mumbles under her breath.

'Beth? It's Jim.'

She casts an apologetic look Robin's way. 'He's a regular. He can come in, right? He just wants his morning pint. He'll stay away from the kitchen.'

Robin agrees, and the old man shambles into the pub. He takes a high stool; Beth expertly pours him his Guinness, placing it on the bar in front of him.

'Keeps me healthy,' he says, with a grin, and Robin can well believe it. He has big hairy ears, a few sparse strands on his head, face tanned like leather. He takes his muddy jacket off, revealing an old fleece underneath, grass stains ingrained. 'Sorry about the state of me,' he says. 'Came from the allotment. Are you the police Beth was telling me about?'

Robin nods and sits next to him at the bar. He's happy to take the weight off, letting Freya do the supervision in the kitchen.

'Do you want anything, Detective?' Beth asks. 'I can do you a coffee. If Guinness is too much for you at this hour.'

'Yes, please,' he replies. 'Have you known Beth long?' he asks Jim.

'A bit,' he confirms, with a smile towards her. 'Been coming here since Kevin ran the place. Awful news,' he says, his mouth downturned. 'I always wondered what happened to him. Good bloke.'

'What was he like?' Robin asks.

'He lived for Bethie. Always told me about her calls, what she was up to, her success at uni. Proud dad. He had an eye for the ladies, though.' Jim laughs. 'Running a pub was the perfect job for him. Charming sod.'

'Any women in particular?'

'No. Whoever would have him. No one special.'

'Did you know the staff that worked here at that time?' Robin says hopefully, and his optimism is rewarded as Jim nods. 'A woman called Sara Gold? She would have been about twenty? Uni student?'

'Was she one of that group? Those kids that used to come here?'

Robin feels the apprehension. 'Possibly. Tell me more?'

'Four. No, five of them. Three blokes and two women. They came here because one of them worked behind the bar. Not sure which, though, Kevin was fairly lax about those things. He let you serve yourself if he'd had a few.' He laughs. 'He said, as long as I only have to pay one of them, and the other four are drinking, the profits take care of themselves. Although…'

Jim pauses, his pint half raised to his lips, thinking.

'What?' Robin prompts.

Jim scowls. 'They had this big fight. Not all of them – but the others had to intervene. Separate them.'

'The blokes were fighting?'

'No, no, not the boys. The couple. Looked alike, they did. Same colour hair, similar names. I always joked they could be brother and sister.'

'Sara and Sam?'

Jim frowns again. 'Could be. It was a long time ago. But they went at it. She was punching him, hitting him. Kevin said later the lad had broken up with her but whatever it was, she didn't take it well. Kev had to throw them all out.'

'Did you see them again after that?' Robin asks.

'No. And Kev fired the one who worked here. He said he didn't want the hassle, students scrapping. Then Kev went missing and, well...' He shrugs. 'It all changed.' He turns back to his Guinness with a grin. 'I still come, though. Rain or shine, it's good to get out.'

'Robin?' Freya pokes her head out from the kitchen, then joins him in the bar.

Robin pats the guy on the shoulder. 'Thank you for your help,' he says. 'I might get someone to take a statement of what you've said, if that's okay.'

Jim nods. 'I'll be here,' he repeats. 'Rain or shine.'

Robin smiles, then follows Freya to the far side of the bar.

'How's it going in there?' he asks.

'Good. Jess will fill you in. But listen, Robin.' She pauses, biting her lip.

'What is it?' He's worried. Something seems wrong.

She looks up, meeting his eyes. 'I need to talk to you. About something important.'

'Now?'

'No, not now. But soon. Please?'

'Any time. You know that, Frey.' He reaches out to reassure her, but she moves away. He frowns, feeling a strangeness between them. He instinctively knows that whatever it is, he's not going to like it.

'Let's go and speak to Jess,' Freya says, and walks quickly back to the kitchen. He follows.

It's a tiny room: a sink and fridge on one side, cupboards and a narrow food prep area on the other. The smallness of the space is emphasised by the number of people in it: two SOCOs in white suits, on their knees, Freya in the doorway. Robin stands behind her, looking over her shoulder.

'So, Butler,' Jess says. She sits back on her knees, speaking through the white mask she's wearing. 'Most of this room was renovated when Miss Gillis took over in 2000, but luckily she only replaced the doors of the cupboards. And,' she adds, 'they put down lino on the kitchen floor, rather than tiles, so we've been able to pull it up with ease.'

Robin looks at the floor, slightly grubby, stripped back.

'And?' he asks. 'Have we found anything that makes this destruction worthwhile?'

'But of course,' she says, her eyes crinkling with amusement. 'Don't doubt my abilities. Considering the amount of blood estimated on the body wrapping and Dr Harper's assessment at the PM, we expected to find quite a bit of blood spatter. We were right.' She points to the edge of the cupboards. 'Blood traces all around here, where it seeped down the edge of the original lino, plus some spatters inside. No knife, though,' she adds.

Robin shrugs. 'That's okay. We didn't expect it. Do you think this is where he was killed?' he asks.

Jess smiles again. 'Absolutely.' He can sense her job satisfaction, the thrill of having their suspicions confirmed. 'DS Butler,' she finishes, standing up and snapping her plastic gloves off her hands. 'You have a crime scene.'

32

DCI Baker's expression is inscrutable. He stares at Freya and Robin, as Robin explains what they've found, the link between the two cases.

'But you have no proof?' Baker says at last. 'No evidence that ties them together?'

'No.'

'Just a load of weird behaviour and an intersecting timeline?'

'Yes. But guv,' Robin continues. 'They have to be linked. We dig into the old murder—'

'The theoretical murder.'

'How else did that body get in the ground? And all that blood spatter in that pub?' Robin counters, and Baker makes a gesture to say, sure, carry on.

'Then we might find something that helps with present day. Give us a few days. A week tops.'

Freya waits while Baker thinks. It's in meetings like this that she appreciates working for Robin. He has a way about him, a calm confidence in what he's doing, that commands people to listen. She knows she talks too fast; she gets muddled when the attention is on her. But Robin? Nothing fazes Robin.

Freya sits up straight, thinking back to their five suspects. 'And don't you think it's odd?' she begins. 'That none of them have healthy interpersonal relationships?'

The two men shift their attention to her. 'Sara and Mike Williams are getting divorced because one of them had an affair. Meg is single. Alex was, too. None of them have a life. Except Sam Bowen, who goes the other way entirely and lives to excess.'

'What are you saying, West?' Baker asks.

'That they're all a bit fucked up.' She points a finger at their photos. The bundle she's found herself carrying around with her all the time. Reminders of the people they once were. 'What if...' she says. 'What if something happened at the end of university that involved Kevin Gillis? Something that screwed them up, which meant they never spoke again. Then Alex Reynolds receives a terminal cancer diagnosis and is determined to get the gang back together.' She remembers her name, written in his notebook. 'Even go to the police.'

'It's Christmas,' Robin adds. 'We don't have any other cases. Nothing new coming in. What have we got to lose?'

'Tell me about it,' Baker mutters. 'The press are nagging me for something they can write about. Fine,' he agrees at last. That's the other thing that Freya has noticed: Baker lets Robin follow his instincts. More so than he does with any other detective. She knows Robin and Baker go way back, that their relationship is more personal than is common between DCI and a DS under his command. But it works in their favour. And who is she kidding? There's nothing usual about her and Robin together either, their partnership bonded by the secrets they continue to keep.

'Have a look,' Baker continues. 'But keep it simple – and cheap. Don't go splashing my budget around on a whim. And update Mouse when he gets back from Cornwall or whatever wood-burning stove he's curled up in front of right now.'

They both nod and leave Baker, before he changes his mind.

'We need evidence,' Robin says as the two of them walk back to the office. 'Proof, and fast. How do you feel about working with Josh?'

'Fine,' Freya replies. What about you? she thinks but stays quiet.

'We'll get you covering different lines of enquiry, don't worry. You start with Sara and Mike Williams. I want to know who she was having an affair with. And get on to Intel and see if they've got any further with her employment records. Confirm the date she was fired.'

'Yes, Sarge.'

'I'll get Josh and Mina digging into the events twenty years ago. Now they have an ID, they might be able to find someone else who remembers Kevin Gillis.'

Freya sits down at her desk and watches Robin as he goes over to talk to Josh. She flinches at the expression on Josh's face. He's not happy, being under Robin's orders.

This is not going to help their already strained relationship, she thinks. This is not going to help at all.

33

The man's still talking. Droning on in that annoying monotone, the same way he has every Wednesday afternoon for weeks. Sam's not listening. To be fair, he doesn't need to – it's the same story. How his ex-wife chewed him up and spat him out, leaving him crying on his kitchen floor. How he still loves her. How he misses her. For fuck's sake. It's no wonder the poor woman left if this is the shit she had to endure.

But this man is the exception. The limit of his empathy. For the most part, Sam likes being a therapist. A front-row seat to the rich tapestry of human fragility and failure. And generally, he can help. Listen, guide and carve them back into fully functioning social beings.

He's seen, first-hand, how damaging trauma can be. How it affects people differently. Some retreat into themselves, recoiling from the slightest touch. While others resort to violence or hate. He knows how he changed. Constructed a hard shell of indifferent sarcasm, using his intelligence and scorn to keep people away. He hadn't been able to help anyone, then, but he could sure as hell have a go with others, now.

Except this guy. Fuck, he's a wanker. Sam's aware he's looking at him, expecting some sort of response to the diatribe.

Sam clears his throat. 'And how did that make you feel?' he asks, generically. But it works, and off the man goes again.

Sam tries to concentrate. He does. But he's been off his game since Alex got back in touch. It hadn't taken a genius to work out what Alex wanted to talk about, why he wanted them all back together. And now he's dead.

Sam tries to rationalise Alex's death. Logical thinking, that's Sam's forte. Alex had been dying anyway. It's not like he had kids or a family; there was no one going hungry as a result. What difference does it make to Sam? He hadn't seen Alex for twenty years, so his absence shouldn't make a ripple in Sam's life.

But it has. It fucking has. Sam finds himself waking at night with a jolt. Dreams of Alex, his grin, his raucous laugh, and he misses him anew. He lies awake in the darkness, his own mortality playing on his mind.

What if Sam died? Who would miss him? His ex-wives maybe, but only for the alimony. Not his daughter, that was for sure; he's never been a part of her life. He resolves it's time to pull his finger out. Grow up. Make an effort. Put his heart on the line without hesitation.

Alex never had. Sam could guess why. A fear that getting close to someone might cause you to reveal the truth. A part of your life you keep hidden.

He'd always liked Alex. They shared the same sense of humour, an enjoyment of silly pranks and word games, sometimes at the expense of others. But where Sam could go too far, potentially offend, Alex knew when to pull back from the brink. His sense of right and wrong was clear – a factor Sam worries has played a part in his premature demise.

Someone wanted him dead. Someone who knew what happened back then. And now the police are sniffing around, so close that Sam can feel their warm breath on the back of his neck.

It's only a matter of time. But Sam worries, who will get there first? He feels a shiver of fear run down his spine. Someone killed Alex. How long before they try again? To kill the other people who know.

34

'As motives go, it's not a great one,' Freya says. They're sat in Robin's car, parallel-parked along the main road in Portswood. 'Killing the owner of the bar for firing you.'

It's dark outside, as night has fallen while they've been sat there. Their enquiries that day have all met with dead ends: Victoria from Intel could only confirm the final date of Sara Williams' employment at the Dog and Duck as the second of June 2000. Something they pretty much knew anyway. They are waiting on the lab, and on Steph to come back with more on the knife.

Freya has been avoiding Josh. And Mina, who has a sixth sense for these things, has also been giving her strange looks. So when Robin suggested taking a recce out to Portswood at night, to check out the scene of the crime, as it were, she jumped at the chance.

'Yes, but you have to admit, it fits,' Robin replies. He takes a large bite out of the burger in his hand, then continues, his mouth full. 'Even if it is a bit of an overreaction.' He looks at Freya and she shrugs. 'On a different thread, Sara clearly has a history with Sam.'

Robin had told Freya about his conversation with the regular at the bar, the argument between Sara and Sam.

'Do you think he's the reason for their divorce?' Freya suggests. 'The legal documents cite infidelity. We could try to prove it?'

'How would that help?'

'Motive for Christmas Eve? Maybe Sam was trying to kill Mike? Or Sara was?'

'But they are getting divorced.'

'Maybe they didn't know that. Mike hadn't filed the papers yet, had he?' She picks at her own burger, pulling the gherkin out and dropping it in Robin's tray next to his chips. He eats it without comment. 'Or maybe they did know about it, and Sara wanted to kill Alex and Mike as revenge?'

'For asking for a divorce?' Robin laughs. 'Sure, why not? People have killed for less. But in such a public, risky fashion? Taking herself and the others down at the same time?'

Freya has no answer for that. It's a shit hypothesis, and she knows it.

They continue to eat in silence, looking out into the darkened streets. It's cold. The few people that are out walk quickly, shoulders hunched, hands thrust in pockets.

'How did they move the body anyway?' Robin says, his attention switching back to the cold case. He points towards the pub, then in the direction of the Waitrose car park. 'In June, a nice warm night, there would have been people everywhere. You can't lug a large roll of lino full of a bloody, dead body without anyone noticing.'

'Early hours of the morning?' Freya suggests.

'Perhaps. It would have been heavy. Sara Williams couldn't have done it on her own.'

'True.'

Robin finishes his burger and wipes his hands. He starts the engine and pulls out of the parking space, heading towards Waitrose. He makes the turn, then again, through the big iron gates into the car park.

Freya puts the remains of her burger down in the polystyrene tray in her lap. She's lost her appetite. She had another reason for agreeing to Robin's field trip: she wanted to get him alone.

She can feel her heart beating hard, body already in fight or flight, in preparation for his reaction. 'Robin?' she begins.

'Hmm?' He's rotated in his seat, reversing the Volvo into a parking space.

She waits, not wanting him to put another dent in the old car. He stops and puts the handbrake on.

'I need to talk to you.'

'Okay.'

But before she can speak, his phone rings. His face is apologetic as he answers.

'Jess? That was quick.' He puts her on loudspeaker and her voice fills the car.

'Blood results from the pub aren't back yet. I'm good, but not that good. It's about the hip flask found at the scene. We found Meg Carlton's prints. And only her prints.'

'So she *was* drinking.'

'That's just it. When we tested the rest of the bottles and cans collected that night, we found the alcohol we expected. But the flask – that contained water. Not that much was left.'

'Water? And that was all?' Robin asks. He glances to Freya; she sees her confusion mirrored on his face.

'Good old H2O.'

'Odd,' Robin replies. Jess says her goodbyes and hangs up. 'So why would Meg Carlton fill a flask with water?' he directs to Freya.

Freya shrugs blankly. Her rehearsed words from earlier hang in her mind, blocking any other coherent response.

Robin stares at her. Then his forehead furrows. 'Is this about Smith?' he asks.

'Kind of.'

He waits as she pulls herself together.

'After we saw Elise, after I spoke to you, I did as you said and asked him.'

'And?'

'It wasn't about her.' She shakes her head, trying to unscramble the muddle in her brain. 'We argued. Long story short, he says I'm holding back. That there are things in my life I'm keeping to myself.'

'Jonathan.'

She nods, slowly. 'I need to tell him.'

A silence descends in the car. Freya is suddenly all too aware of the people outside their window, shoppers going about their normal lives. Matters like murder and career-ending lies not impacting them in any way.

Robin hasn't said anything. He's staring out of the windscreen, his face lit by the glow from the front of the store.

'What are you going to say?' he asks slowly.

He turns and looks at her, the strange lighting bringing out the green in his usually mottled-brown eyes.

'He knows I'm hiding something. But I won't mention you, Robin,' she says quickly. 'I'll say you didn't know. That it was all my doing.'

'And he'll believe that? He won't dig up the case files and see that we knew that Jonathan Miller had a bit on the side?' Freya flinches at his expression. She knows Robin has put that in deliberately, out of anger. 'And he won't twig that the DS in charge conveniently forgot that bit in the official statement? And then what, Freya? Won't he wonder why I didn't report you?'

She runs her hands down her face. Her skin feels dry, paper-thin. All this, all that he's saying, she knows.

'What else can I do, Robin?'

'Make some shit up,' he snaps. 'Tell him to mind his own bloody business, I don't know. But you can't tell him. Come on, Freya! I might not like the guy much, but he's not stupid. He'll work it out. And what then? He traces it all back to the other case you were working on at that time? The one involving my sister?'

Freya opens her mouth to talk, then closes it again. Robin's right. Fuck, he's so right.

Fifteen months ago, in the middle of Jonathan's murder investigation, she was briefly seconded to review a closed case. One involving the death of the man who caused the hit-and-run that killed Robin's sister and her twin boys. Freya found out the truth about what happened when that man died. Truth that implicated Robin in a crime more serious than her own indiscretion.

'I won't put you at risk,' she whispers.

He stares at her for a moment longer, then shifts his gaze outside. Slowly, he puts his hands on the steering wheel; he grips it so hard his knuckles turn white. She doesn't talk, waiting for him to say something more. Anything. To present a solution. A way forward that doesn't involve putting both their futures on the line.

'It's late. I'll drop you back,' he says at last.

He starts the engine and they drive out of the car park, back to the nick. She stares out of the window as they pass familiar streets, busy traffic. She feels a hollow in the pit of her stomach, knots in her muscles. She feels horrible for what she is putting him through.

What had she expected? That he would agree? She knows she is being insane, that she has no way of knowing how Josh will react. They've only been together six months. He says he loves her, but how much? Enough to overlook that she broke all the rules, lied about the fact that the man she loved was the victim of the very murder she was investigating?

They pull up in the car park of the police station and Robin puts the handbrake on. She looks over to him, taking her seat belt off.

'I'm sorry, Robin,' she says. But she doesn't know what she's apologising for.

'Freya,' he begins. He doesn't look at her. He breathes out slowly, his chest emptying. 'I know I don't have any say in this. I have no right to tell you what to do, how to deal with Josh's request. I don't matter.' He pulls a face, looking up. For a moment, she thinks he's upset but when he looks at her, his eyes are dry. 'Think about it. Please. Think of everything you have to lose.'

She nods and gets out of the car, shutting the door. She watches as he drives away, the damaged bumper of the old Volvo banging ominously as the car turns the corner out of sight.

She knew she could lose Josh in all of this. She knew she could lose her job. But it never crossed her mind that she might lose Robin, too.

35

After Robin drops Freya at the station, he feels strange. Lost. The sudden weightlessness of being thrown off a cliff, waiting to hit the ground. He drives round for a while, taking junctions and roundabouts randomly, the motion of changing gear lulling him into a calm.

He needs something to distract him. He needs to think about the case.

He takes the next turn, heading towards Sara Williams' house. It's getting late now, nearly ten, and the quiet residential street is empty. He looks up at the windows; most are in darkness, only one downstairs is lit.

He silences the engine, turns off the lights. He sits in the darkness, listening to the tick of the car engine cooling. The air is colder now, and he zips his coat up, pulling the collar high round his ears. Gloves on his hands. Hat on his head. He waits.

He's not sure what he's watching for. He's assuming Sara Williams is in there. Visiting hours are over at the hospital, but she could be with friends, family. The house could be empty.

He still can't get on board with Freya's theory: that Sara would try to kill her own husband because he's filing for divorce. There are better ways of doing it. Morphine overdoses on quiet, cold beaches are far from reliable, as has been proven. And there were three other people there.

Maybe it was an accident. Maybe it was coincidence that Sara had worked in the bar where the man had disappeared. Maybe, maybe, he thinks. If only they could prove *something*.

His mind drifts to Freya. Is she telling Josh now? Tonight? He feels the ball of nerves grow in his stomach. The bitter taste of anger towards her for being so stupid. For thinking that her relationship problems can be solved with this hard bolt of honesty, when the only thing it can possibly do is make it worse. Someone like Josh Smith, with his charming smile and golden life, could never understand the situation Freya had been in. What love, and loss, and the hot burn of revenge can make you do. Josh has never experienced hardship is his life. If she's lucky, he will judge Freya and she'll come out lacking. If it goes the other way, he could take all his righteousness and report her.

And then where would it go? To Professional Standards. Maybe to the IOPC. They'd investigate and they'd come across Robin. And what he did.

Both their lives would be over, and for what? So Joshua-bloody-Smith could feel a little bit more included in his girlfriend's life? For fuck's sake.

While Robin is brooding, a red sports car cruises down the road. He recognises the logo on the grill, the gorgeous curves of an Audi R8. A new one, too; Robin guesses six figures' worth of supercar, right there.

He scoots lower in his seat as the car slides to a stop in the Williams' driveway. He waits. The door opens, a man gets out. Sam Bowen.

He's walking quickly, long black coat pulled round tight. He glances up at the dark windows before pressing the doorbell. Sara Williams, wearing jeans and a jumper, opens the door. Robin takes a few photos on his phone as she looks out into the darkened road, then kisses Sam. Quickly, but on the lips, no mistaking the intention. He pushes her into the house. The front door closes.

So, the old boyfriend is back. Robin sits and waits; it's not hard to imagine what's going on in that house. Lights turn on upstairs, curtains are hastily closed by a part-clothed Sara. It's hardly discreet and, some might say, uncaring. Her husband is in hospital, prognosis uncertain, and she's hooking up with her university sweetheart? But then, if they are responsible for what happened on Christmas Eve, a bit of casual sex isn't the worst thing they've done in the past week.

He holds his phone in his hand, about to text Freya, but he stops. He'll leave her tonight. He hopes she's alone, thinking through what she's about to do. Reconsidering her decision to implode their lives.

For so long after the events of six years ago, he felt he was falling. Waiting to hit the ground. But then Freya came along, and he finally allowed himself to relax. She had been his parachute. With her calm understanding, her friendship, her company. He might break a leg, but he would recover; it wouldn't be the bone-mushing collapse he expected.

But now, with Freya's words, he feels it all returning. In one conversation, she's dragged him to the cliff, her hands on his back, ready to push him over.

He starts his car again, driving away from the house. But he doesn't get far. He pulls into a side street, his fingers resting lightly on the gearstick, putting it into neutral. Handbrake on. And then, slowly, his hands ball into fists, and he punches, hard, again and again, putting all his strength into the rigid plastic of the steering wheel.

36

Thursday

Freya wakes, groggy, to a text from Robin.

Pick you up, 8am

Then a follow-up: *Are you at home?*

She replies. *Yes.*

Freya sat in the car park at the police station for a while after Robin left. Thinking. Desperate to call Josh, but not knowing what to say. She wonders what's going on in his mind. He can't be happy about having to work for Robin, but she's not about to start bad-mouthing her boss to appease her boyfriend. Yes, Robin's style leaves something to be desired, especially where Josh is concerned, but Robin knows what he's doing. He's good at his job.

But the intersection now between what Josh wants and the inevitable impact on Robin leaves her at an impasse. Robin's right – telling Josh about Jonathan would be disastrous. But not telling him? As her boyfriend, does Josh have a right to know about her past, or are there some things in a relationship you're entitled to keep quiet?

She hadn't come to any conclusions, sitting in the cold, draughty police station car park, so she'd driven home. Eventually putting herself to bed after two large glasses of white and four episodes of *Friends*. Glasses of wine she now regrets, as she hauls herself into the shower to get ready for Robin.

When he arrives, he's his usual self; there are no outward signs of the discussion they had last night. He hands her a coffee as she gets in, regarding her from beneath lowered brows.

'Late night?' he asks.

'Couldn't sleep,' she mumbles to the coffee. He nods and starts to drive. 'Where are we going?'

Eyes on the road, he hands her his phone. It's open to a photograph. She squints at it, then looks at him, astonished.

'That's Sara Williams' house,' she says.

'And that's Sam Bowen.'

'When was this?'

'Last night.'

She stares at the photo, worrying about Robin's foray out alone. She knows that when he does things without her on a case, they're often on a whim, ending badly.

'Did you speak to them?' she asks.

'No. They're definitely together, though.' He takes a turn off a roundabout and Freya figures out where they're going. 'Thought it was time we have a chat with Mike Williams,' Robin confirms.

–

Michael Williams has been moved to a normal ward. Robin and Freya peel off layers as they approach, the heating stifling and only serving to emphasise the pervading smell of disinfectant. He sits alone at the far end, next to the window. It's open a fraction, the breeze blowing the curtains.

He's wearing a grey T-shirt, a blanket covering his legs. His appearance is a direct contrast to his fair-haired wife. Brown, almost black hair, tanned skin, dark stubble. His hands lie helpless, white bandages covering them in their entirety. He doesn't look up as they approach.

'Michael Williams?' Robin says.

He turns. His eyes are dull, hooded.

'DS Robin Butler, DC Freya West.' Freya holds out her ID, but Williams' gaze is blank. 'Can we join you?'

He nods to the chair. Robin gestures to Freya and she sits down.

'We were hoping you would talk to us,' Freya begins, gently. 'So we can find out what happened to you.'

'I don't know what happened to me,' Michael says, monotone.

'Could you tell us what you know?'

'Nothing. I don't remember anything. We arrived at the beach, Sara and I. We were the last to arrive. We sat down with the others, shared a few drinks.'

'A few?' Robin asks. 'There were more than a few empty bottles on that beach.'

Mike stops, then slowly looks up at Robin. 'The vodka, that was Sam's. The whisky was Alex's, he shared it with me.'

'And what time was this?'

'Until late. I remember midnight: Alex said, "Merry Christmas". Then – nothing.' He stares at Freya. 'I wondered when you'd be here. Sara said you've been asking questions.'

'We were waiting for you to recover.'

'Recover?' Mike lifts his hands up to show her. 'You call this recovery? I'm a fucking human cotton bud. Sticking me on pain meds, waiting to see what will happen before they decide. When to cut my fingers off...' His voice breaks. 'Leaving me with stumps, that's all I'll have left.'

'We're sorry, Michael,' Freya says softly.

'Yeah, well.' He lowers his hands, gently placing them in his lap. 'If you're so sorry then you can arrest that bastard.'

'Who?' Freya glances up to Robin.

'Sam, that's who.'

'He did this?'

'Who else?' Michael is animated now, his face contorting with anger. 'It's just his sort of thing. Something he'd find funny. Inflict pain and watch to see how we'll react. Fucking sociopath. Have you worked out what we consumed? Apart from the booze?'

'We believe it was morphine, Mr Williams.'

'Where...' he starts. Then he looks at them. 'It was Alex's, right?'

'Yes.'

Williams frowns.

'Did Sam have access to Alex's house?'

'Not as far as I know, no,' he replies, quieter again. 'Alex and Sam weren't in touch. The first time they met again was at the beach.'

'And when was the last time you'd seen Sam?'

'Oh, Christ. A long time ago. Just after uni.'

'And Alex?'

Mike Williams looks at them closely. 'You know, don't you? About the divorce papers?' Freya nods. 'I used to be a cop – you know that, too, I assume? Fifteen years, working my way up to Inspector. So I know what you're doing. Know how you think.'

'Why did you leave?' Robin asks.

'Bureaucracy. Erosion of pay and benefits.' He shrugs. 'The usual. I work for myself now as a security consultant.'

'And what does that involve?'

'I assess residential and commercial properties for potential risk, both cyber and physical threats. Keeping people safe.'

'That's all we're trying to do too, Mr Williams. We just want to find out what happened,' Freya repeats. She waits, watching Mike. After a moment, he sighs.

'Alex and I had been in touch on and off over the years. Not regularly. I think we met up maybe twice. But when I needed a lawyer, I called him. He said it wasn't his area, but he'd help me out as much as he could.'

'When was this?'

'After the summer. The kids were back at school, so yes, it would have been September. And I knew about Alex's diagnosis, if that's where you're going next. But I didn't know he was as sick as he was. He hid it well.'

'Do you have any reason to think Alex would kill himself?'

Mike looks up sharply. 'Alex? No. That's not what happened. He had things he wanted to do before he died. He'd tell me about them. Great long lists.' His face turns sad. 'Poor Al. No, that wasn't his plan at all.'

'Was meeting up with his old uni friends one of them?'

Mike pauses. 'I guess so, yes,' he says after a beat.

'Why hadn't you seen them in such a long time?'

'We grew apart. That's all.' While Mike Williams has been considering his answers up to this point, slow and thoughtful, the last sentence is blurted out quickly. A story recited a thousand times.

'Why are you divorcing your wife, Mr Williams?' Robin asks.

'Why does anyone get divorced?' He glances to their hands; Freya sees him looking at the space where their wedding rings should be. 'Not that either of you would know.' He sighs. 'I caught her out in a lie. She said she was out with friends, but when I asked on the school run, they knew nothing about it. They tried to cover for her, but by then, I knew.'

'Who was she having an affair with?' Freya asks.

'I don't know. She wouldn't tell me.'

'Does she know you're filing for divorce?'

'Yes. Hard to avoid the subject when you've already started packing.' He pauses, thinking. 'Do you know?' he asks. 'Who he is?'

Freya tries hard to keep her face impassive. She feels Robin's glance.

Mike sees their expressions. 'You do?' He goes to lift his hand to his mouth in an automatic gesture of surprise, then lowers it again with a gasp of pain. 'Who is it? Is she still seeing him?' Freya feels her face get hot. Considering the number of lies she's told, she should be better at it by now. 'Oh, god, it's him, isn't it?' He lets out a long sigh, closing his eyes for a second. 'I should have known. Fucking Bowen. He could have any woman he wants, and instead he has to go back to her.'

'They were together when you were at university?' Freya says, not bothering to deny the assumption he's made.

'Yeah. For years.'

'When did they split up?'

He shakes his head. 'After. I don't remember the exact time. Shit. Why didn't I realise?' He looks at them. 'I loved her once, so much. When we first got married. I thought that nothing could break us, that there was nothing we couldn't survive together. It sucks being wrong.'

He lowers his eyes back to his hands. Freya feels a tap on her shoulder.

'Thank you, Mr Williams,' she says. 'We'll be back in touch soon.'

They walk quickly away from the bedside.

'All we succeeded in doing there,' Freya comments, 'was making everything worse.'

'Their marriage was buggered already. Why does it matter who she was sleeping with? Sounds like there was no love lost between him and Sam Bowen.'

'Why, do you think?'

Robin pauses in the corridor. 'Nobody likes their loved one's past passions,' he says.

Freya looks up at him, taking his comment as a personal dig towards her. About Josh and Jonathan. But he's not paying attention, distracted by something in the distance. She follows his line of sight.

'Who's that?' she says, squinting at the dark-haired figure who has grabbed his focus.

Robin pulls her to the edge of the corridor, both of them quickly turning their backs. But the woman seems preoccupied, hurrying past without a second glance.

'Meg Carlton,' Robin replies.

37

She can only be there for one person: Mike Williams. Robin watches her go, turning down the corridor they've just left.

'So, they're friends,' Freya says once she's out of sight. 'We knew that. We can't see the crime in everything.'

'Freya, that is literally our job,' Robin replies drily as his phone rings. It's Steph.

'Give me some good news,' he says as he answers.

'I'm phoning about the knife,' Steph confirms. 'Blade is approximately two centimetres in width. And pretty solid to go through all that bone and muscle.'

Robin estimates the distance between his finger and thumb. Freya watches him with interest. 'A kitchen knife?' he asks.

'Possibly,' Steph answers. 'That would be consistent with the piece of metal the lab found in the debris round the body.'

'Sorry, what?' Robin glances at Freya. She raises an eyebrow. 'Metal found by the lab?' he whispers to her. She nods.

At the other end of the phone, Steph sighs. 'Read your emails, Butler,' she says, then hangs up.

Robin looks to Freya, accusingly.

'Jess told me,' Freya says. 'She sent you the report. I assumed you would have read it.'

'No, I was...' *distracted last night*, he goes to say, but doesn't want to bring up their conversation again. 'Busy,' he finishes instead.

'There was a piece of metal,' Freya explains. 'They guessed it came from the tip of the knife, broken off and embedded in tissue. And then separated over time, as the biological processes worked their magic.'

'Was there anything else in the rubble?'

'No. And she said the only blood on the lino belonged to Kevin Gillis. Plus, the disintegrated scraps of fabric around the bones weren't recognisable as clothing, let alone conduits to capture any fibres from a killer.'

'So it doesn't help us at all.'

'No.'

They stand in silence for a moment, staring down the deserted corridor. Robin can't help feeling dispirited, and more than a little bit desperate. They're not making any inroads into this investigation at all.

But before he can sulk further, they hear footsteps and Meg heads back their way. She sees them this time: Robin gives her a broad smile, but she just scowls and increases her pace.

'That was quick,' Freya comments.

'Wasn't it?' He can't help the cheeky grin as he turns to Freya. 'Shall we see where she goes?'

-

After overcoming mild resistance from Freya, they walk back to the car park, Meg a short distance in front of them. She gets into the little white Nissan Leaf – a car Robin remembers seeing at the beach on that Christmas Day morning – and drives back towards town.

Robin follows at a respectful distance, but she's slow; it's not hard to keep on her tail. Eventually, she stops outside a small terraced house. There are a few shrubs in pots by the doorway, and a brightly painted window box, empty in the freezing temperatures of December.

Meg gets out and goes through the red front door without a second glance.

'She's gone home,' Freya comments. 'Big deal.'

But Robin's already opening his car door.

'Robin!' Freya hisses. 'We can't go in there.'

'Why not? We can just knock. See if she wants to talk.' Freya's face is dubious. 'You said it yourself. Out of the four, she's our most likely candidate for cracking. Remember how close she was to talking back at the station?' He pauses. 'Look, she can only say no.'

Freya frowns, but pulls her coat around her, ready to move. 'I could really do without a harassment complaint on my record, right now,' she mutters, getting out of the car.

Robin knocks. They wait. They hear soft footsteps and the door opens a crack, the safety chain on.

'I don't want to talk to you,' Meg says, and goes to close the door.

'Meg, please,' Robin tries, quickly, before the door shuts. 'We just want to make sure that you're okay. That whoever did this to Alex won't hurt you again.'

It's bollocks, and Robin knows it. But Meg hesitates, the door opening a fraction. Robin continues: 'Please, Meg. We're worried about you.'

'I'm fine,' she whispers.

'Tell us what happened on Christmas Eve. If not for you, then for Alex.'

Robin waits. He feels a pull on his sleeve from Freya behind him, but then the door closes and there's the rattle of the chain being removed.

They're in.

38

Meg saw them follow her. From half-closed curtains, she watched the detectives pull up outside her house. Everything about them puts her on edge. From their disposable coffee cups, noticeably discarded in the footwell of the black Volvo, to the woman's long blonde hair. It reminds her of Sara all those years ago.

But despite herself, she's starting to like the man, Butler. His determination to do what's right for Alex. His worry for her. It's nice, that someone cares. For a change.

She shows them through, apologising as DS Butler trips over the pile of Cancer Research branded bin bags in the doorway.

'Clothes for charity,' she says, cursing herself for not taking them out to the car earlier. 'Had a big clear-out. Don't like anything to go to waste.'

Her two large fluffy tabby cats appear and wind themselves around Butler's legs. Meg reaches over and picks one up.

She debates offering them tea or coffee but doesn't want them to stay any longer than is necessary. She'll tell them more about what happened that night, then they'll go. They'll be happy; a big tick against her name for co-operating with the police. That won't hurt, surely?

They all sit down. Meg places the cat on her lap, taking reassurance in its soft fur. It purrs loudly.

'What happened on Christmas Eve, Meg?' Butler asks softly.

She takes a long breath in. 'Alex phoned. Wanted us all to get together. And the others took some persuasion, I can tell you. But once they all knew about… about his cancer, that he was dying, nobody could possibly say no. He said he wanted one last drinking session with his oldest friends. He had this massive bottle of whisky with him.'

'Did any of you suggest to Alex that drinking wasn't a good idea in his condition?'

'Of course! We weren't stupid. But Alex said it was up to him, so we let it go. At first, nobody except Sam was keen – he had a bottle of expensive vodka and was passing it around – but eventually we all got into it. Mike shared the whisky with Alex, plus a bit of the vodka. Sara got these cans of some horrid cocktail out of the boot of her car – she said they were left over after some PTA function. I had those, while she had Sam's vodka.' She shrugs. 'It was fun. Reminiscing about the old days.'

'At university?'

'Yeah.'

'But what about your cars?' West asks. 'You can't possibly have been planning to drive home?'

'Not straight away, no. But none of us had anywhere to be the next day. Sara and Mike's kids were at her parents', and they were going to get a taxi there, and the rest of us, well…' Meg pauses. She runs her hands down from the cat's head to its warm body, taking solace in the repetitive action. 'My dad lives abroad,' she confesses. 'I don't have any other family. Never did, except for these guys. We used to do it in the old days, too. Stay the night on the beach, sometimes sheltering in the beach hut. Like puppies, Alex would say. Sleeping on top of each other for warmth. And in the morning, Sam would drive us home.'

She catches a glance from West to Butler. Sure, Sam was probably over the limit, back then. But they can't prove that now, can they?

'Weren't you cold?'

'Yeah, a bit. But once the alcohol kicked in, we were okay. Sam was singing silly songs; when it got freezing later on, Alex remembered the hot chocolate in the car and we passed it around. You don't notice the cold when you're having fun. And Alex was happy. I was glad we could be there for him.'

'And then what?'

'I wish I knew. I woke up, freezing, with that dog in my face. The man gave us blankets, passed me his coat. We were all confused. Then terrified when Alex and Mike didn't wake up.'

Meg remembers the moment when the man tried to revive Alex. But he was cold, so cold, so he turned his efforts to Mike instead. Meg remembers crying, panic turning to relief when the man said that Mike had a pulse. She held him then, tried to warm him up as they waited for the ambulance.

'Who do you think was responsible, Meg? For Alex's death?'

Butler asks it softly. He's leaning forward, his arms resting on his knees. One name springs into Meg's mind. One person, just standing there, shaking, her eyes wide, ignoring her unconscious husband, as Meg held Mike. Her eyes locked on Alex's pale, motionless body.

'Sara,' she replies.

39

Robin looks smug as they get in the car.

'Fifty quid we still get a complaint,' Freya grumbles, as they drive back to the nick. 'And I'm not sure Meg's finger-pointing gets us very far.'

Meg couldn't offer any explanation for her accusation, and certainly not any proof. She clammed up when Robin pushed her further; Freya dragged him away before he could do any more damage.

'Just goes to show their little group isn't as tight as those old photos make out,' Robin replies, making a right turn into the station car park. 'Catch them off guard, they turn on each other.'

Mina appears the moment they arrive in the office. She's clutching a piece of scrap paper.

'Council work order,' she declares triumphantly. 'For the car park.'

'Let me guess,' Freya says. 'It was laid in June 2000.'

'Yes,' Mina replies, her energy dissipated. 'But do you know how many people I had to threaten to get this?'

'I'm sorry,' Freya adds. 'Thank you. At least it doesn't disprove our theory.'

Freya fills Mina in on their conversations with Mike and Meg.

'So your money is still with Sara and Sam? The happy couple?' Mina asks. Robin nods, Freya shrugs. 'But why?'

Freya rubs her eyes with the back of one hand then pulls at her forehead with her fingers. Her skull feels tight, a headache threatening. The lack of sleep last night isn't helping.

'It must all come back to the guy buried in the car park,' Robin comments. 'Covering up a murder would give enough motive to kill. Did you or Josh turn up anything from your door to door?'

'Nothing. And the local paper ran a story this morning, identifying the dead man as Kevin Gillis and asking for help. Still quiet on the tipline.'

Robin sits up straight, looking decisive. 'Have we heard anything back about the warrant for Alex's will?' Mina shakes her head. 'Mina, get on it. Start nagging. I want to know who gets his estate. There might be something of interest there.' Robin looks around quickly. 'And where is Josh?'

'He went to chase up Mike Williams' file with HR,' Mina replies.

'Did he? Good. Frey, can you go and find Greg? See if he's got anything new on the mobile phone.'

She nods, but it's a bullshit request. Freya knows Robin well enough by now: he's up to something. She gets up to go, but then pauses in the corridor, waiting.

Sure enough, barely five minutes later, Robin steams past her, coat in hand. 'Robin,' she shouts, and he stops. His guilty expression is almost enough to make her laugh.

'Don't you dare sneak out alone,' she says. She holds a stern finger in front of his face, and he frowns. 'Wait for me to get my coat. Whatever you're up to, Robin Butler, I'm coming with you.'

40

Freya doesn't ask. She just knows that whatever Robin is doing, he shouldn't be going alone. They get back into his car without debate; she sits wordlessly as he drives towards the city centre, eventually stopping outside a parade of town houses. Posh, white clean brick, gold nameplates next to the doors.

'Sam Bowen's office,' he explains.

She looks up at the building, at the smart sash windows, the white blinds pulled shut against the world. She imagines the conversations going on inside. What do you talk about to a therapist? Where would she even start?

The silence between her and Robin, normally comfortable, has felt wrong all day. She feels like he's being deliberately provocative, pushing her to challenge him, but any words of reassurance stick in her throat, choking her. She still hasn't decided what to do – caught in between what's best for Josh, and the possible destruction of her and Robin.

Robin's phone rings, interrupting her thoughts.

'Josh?' Robin says, putting the phone on loudspeaker. 'Do you have it?'

'Yep.' Josh's voice comes through loud and clear. Just the sound of him makes her heart leap. As sappy as she recognises it is, she really does love this man.

'Felicity was the only one in HR,' Josh continues. 'She downloaded it without much fuss. I think she had a lot on. Not much time to argue.'

Not much inclination either, Freya thinks. She knows Felicity. Young, junior. Keen. And definitely susceptible to the charms of Josh.

'And?' Robin prompts.

'Um…' They can hear the sound of fingers tapping a keyboard. 'A few notes from performance development reviews. An exit interview, hardly in depth. No disciplinary proceedings or complaints. Actually, here, the opposite. He has a commendation from the Assistant Chief Constable.'

'So, a good cop?'

'Absolutely. Nothing shady in Williams' career. Sorry, Sarge.'

Josh hangs up. But before either of them can say anything, the R8 emerges from the underground car park.

Robin puts the car into gear and follows.

-

Traffic is on their side. Had Sam Bowen gained the advantage of the open road, he would have lost them in seconds, but rush hour slows the Audi to a frustrating crawl. And he doesn't go far. He stops after a few miles, a street away from a row of bars that Freya knows well.

'You need a gold credit card just to get in,' Robin mutters. 'That, or a BMI lower than fifteen.'

Freya laughs, and for the first time that day, Robin returns her smile. A moment of connection, where she relaxes and feels a glow of appreciation for him. But it quickly fades.

They watch Sam Bowen go inside, then Robin turns the car around, leaving her staring, open-mouthed, as one of their prime suspects goes out of sight.

'Can't we go in?'

He grunts. 'They wouldn't let me near that place.'

'Can't I?'

Robin turns quickly, a warning look in his eyes. 'No, Freya. Not alone. Not with him. Who knows what he's done?'

He drops her home, dismissing her arguments. She watches him drive off, then she thinks, sod you.

41

Sod you, Freya repeats wordlessly as she puts her make-up on in the mirror. *Sod you*, as she changes her top. Suddenly, she's fed up with all these men telling her what to do. Why should Robin be the only one going on late-night excursions? Why should he be the one having all the fun?

She takes a taxi back into town, walking quickly to the place where they left Bowen. She flashes her best smile to the bouncer and goes in, takes a seat at the bar and orders a drink. A gin and tonic, large. She's not on duty now; she doesn't give a shit.

She takes a sip and looks around. Robin was right: the place is posh, expensive, the people uptight. Even though it's early, there are a good number of people drinking. Giraffe-like women draped with pieces of fabric: high-fashion clothes that look bizarre on mere mortals. Men in expensive suits, shirts gaping at the neck showing impressive expanses of chest hair. It's somewhere Elise would feel at home, Freya thinks with a sting. But no Sam in sight.

It's a wasted trip; he's left already. But as she's debating going, the man next to her leaves and he's there. He's alone, at the end of the bar. He's staring miserably into the pint in front of him, blond hair flopping attractively over his face. He's handsome. He's grown into his looks since university, his jawline now distinct, puppy fat turned into muscle under the stylish suit. She can see what Sara Williams sees in him, compared to her more dishevelled and unrefined husband.

As she watches, a woman approaches. Petite, pretty. A long mane of shiny black hair over large kohl-rimmed eyes. She flirts, touching his arm as she talks. He smiles back, turning his body towards her slightly. So that's it, she thinks. He's here to pick up women. She feels a burn of anger. Sara gave up her marriage for you, and here you are, looking for a cheap shag on a Thursday night. But as she watches, he shakes his head. A look of disappointment appears on the woman's face; she's not used to men saying no.

She stalks back to her friends on the other side of the room, swooshing her hair defiantly.

Freya stares at Sam Bowen. And as she does so, he meets her eye. A look of recognition crosses his face; he lifts his head in acknowledgement. Then he smiles and picks up his drink, heading towards her.

She panics. What should she do? Walk out quickly? Leave now, even though it's clear he knows who she is? No. She'll stay, stand her ground. Brazen it out.

He points to the empty bar stool next to her.

'Is this seat taken, Detective West?'

'Be my guest.'

He sits down slowly. 'What brings you here tonight? Alone?'

His words have an air of menace, but she's in public. There's no threat to her from this man.

'Having a drink. What about you?'

'Same,' he says with a smile. 'And your partner? Your detective sergeant. The grumpy bloke. Where has he gone?'

'Home.'

Sam Bowen nods slowly. 'I see. That's the strategy, is it?'

'What is?'

'A woman like you. My type,' he says. 'Blonde, blue-eyed. Beautiful. More chance of getting me to open up.'

'Is it going to work?'

'I doubt it.' He lifts a finger, waving to the bar staff who come over immediately. 'But since you're here, we might as well enjoy ourselves. A pint of Stella for me. And a G and T for the lady detective, if I'm right in thinking?'

'Yes. Thank you.'

'My pleasure.' The drinks are poured and brought over. Bowen pays with a swipe of his credit card. 'Now, DC West, tell me. How is the investigation going into the death of my friend?'

'Friend?' Freya says. 'You hadn't spoken to Alex Reynolds for twenty years.'

He laughs, throwing his head back to show a set of perfect white teeth. 'So you have done your homework. I'm impressed. And what else do you know?'

'That you and Sara Williams were together. And still are.'

He nods slowly. 'That's correct, too.'

'Is it true love, or convenience?'

'Is that it? Surely, as humans, we are more complicated than that? Or do you only consider two options: soulmates, or a quick fuck?'

Freya stays quiet. She feels nervous, out of her depth with this strange man.

'What about you and your DS?' he continues. 'Which are you?'

She stares at him. 'What do you mean?'

He smiles. 'I have two PhDs and an MSc in social psychology, I'm interested in this sort of stuff. Mixed-gender partnerships. Working so closely together day in, day out. It can do strange things to a platonic relationship.'

Freya takes a sip of her drink. The way he talks, the arrogance, the confidence. That, combined with the two strong drinks on an empty stomach, makes him compelling listening.

'I've seen you twice now. Talking, being together. You and him.'

'Twice?' she says quickly.

'Once at the hospital. And today, in the car. Outside my office?' He grins again. 'You're not that discreet, for cops. You need to work on that.' He takes a sip of his pint. 'I saw the way you were. Easy. In sync, with a kind of shorthand I've seen in all the best partnerships. An interaction that's innate.'

She doesn't dare say anything. She feels him study her.

'Interesting. I'm intrigued.'

'You can stay that way,' Freya snaps. 'It's none of your business.'

'Fair enough. But let me share a little insight that might help you and your sergeant. Even though you say there's nothing going on—'

'There's not.'

He grins again. 'Work partnerships, like yours, can exhibit the same traits. What do you know about interdependence theory, DC West?' He continues, in the face of her silence: 'People try to maximise rewards in any given situation. But these choices are not selfish, and what you do is influenced by things like knowledge of that relationship, concern for your partner's outcomes and your goals for the future. Then you throw in commitment, satisfaction, sacrifice, co-operation, the strength of any alternatives.' He waves his hand, dismissing his complicated explanation. A gesture Freya is starting to dislike. 'What I'm trying to say, simplistically, is that your likelihood of staying in a relationship depends on certain factors. For example, the more you have invested, the more that relationship fulfils important needs, or the more you feel your rewards are equal.'

Freya stares at him. He's talking about her and Robin, but she can't help thinking about Josh. What's stopping him leaving her? She can't imagine he's exactly feeling rewarded right now.

'Answer me one thing about you and your partner. DS Butler, isn't it?'

'Yes.'

'Humour me. One thing.'

'I'll answer your question, on the condition you answer one of mine.'

He smiles, a lopsided grin. 'Deal. Go on then, DC West, tell me. Why do you stay with DS Butler?'

'Because my job tells me I have to.'

'Cop-out. Either of you could request a transfer, I assume?'

'Yes.'

'So why do you stick together? What important need does that relationship fulfil?'

Freya narrows her eyes at him. She thinks about the past year. Everything that happened with Jonathan. The faith he's placed in her.

'Trust,' she replies.

Robin would always have her back, she thinks with a sting of guilt for what she is considering. In that, she has no doubt.

'Go on.'

'We're a team. I know him, how he thinks. I know what he's been through and what a good person he is. That more than makes up for his less desirable traits.'

'And he does the same for you.'

'Yes.'

'And you like him?'

'Yes.'

'More than that?'

'I've answered your question, Mr Bowen. Now it's time for mine.'

Sam laughs. 'Fair enough. Sara. You asked how it is between us. It's love, Detective. Always has been. Always will be.'

'So why did you split up after university?'

A look crosses his face. The cocky smile fades. He stares at his pint for a second. 'Circumstances outside my control,' he says, so quietly Freya has to strain to hear him over the noise of the bar. 'Not my choice.'

'But you got back together? Even after the big fight?'

'Fight?' He frowns. Yes, we know about that, Freya thinks smugly. Then his expression changes to one of sadness, almost wistful. 'It's strange, the passing of time,' he replies. 'You may think things have changed, that you've evolved, grown, got over whatever broke you all those years ago. But one little thing and you're thrown back in an instant. Now.' He smiles broadly, and the arrogance returns. 'If you would be so kind, I must be excused. Work tomorrow.'

He stands up, giving her a little bow. 'I hope to see you again. You and your handsome detective friend.' First, she assumes he's talking about Josh, then realises he means Robin. He pauses, his eyes tilted down. Then he smiles. 'Don't underestimate how complicated love can be, DC West. One thing I've learned from studying people for twenty years is that it's not just about husband and wife, boyfriend and girlfriend. There's obligation and commitment. Promises made, secrets shared, time invested. You work that out, and you'll find your answer, Freya.'

And with that, he walks away. Leaving Freya unsure whether he was talking about the murder of Alex Reynolds, or the relationship between her and Robin.

42

Friday

Freya tosses and turns all night, the sheets growing damp with her sweat. Dreams haunt her: of blond hair and blue eyes, Sara and Sam, spectres in the night, shadowy figures coming to murder her. She wakes suddenly. She's confused, until she realises the phone's ringing.

She picks it up without opening her eyes.

'Robin? Am I late?'

There's a long pause. 'It's Josh,' the voice says. 'Where were you last night?'

'Oh, Josh. I'm sorry.' She opens her eyes and looks at the clock. Seven thirty; she's forgotten to set an alarm. She pulls herself to a sitting position. 'I was out. Working on the case.'

'With Butler?'

'Yes.' A part lie. What's one more? She knows Josh won't approve of her going to the bar alone, of her conversation with Sam Bowen over drinks. 'I'll be in shortly,' she says. 'Shall I get you a coffee?'

Another pause. 'I'm out all today, remember? Butler's sent Mina and me to interview potential witnesses about Kevin Gillis's disappearance.' He sighs. 'Fucking wild goose chase that it is. Who's going to remember this stuff? Twenty years on.'

'It's worth a try,' Freya says, trying to appease him. 'I'm seeing you tonight, right, Josh?'

It's New Year's Eve today. Plans had been made weeks ago to go out with Josh's football mates and their wives. Freya was looking forward to it. That is, until all this happened. Elise, and their argument, and the growing distance between them.

'Yeah. Come to mine for seven?'

Freya agrees. 'I miss you, Josh,' she says quietly.

A long gap. 'I'll see you tonight, Frey.'

He hangs up quickly, leaving Freya staring at the phone in her hand.

–

When she gets into work, Robin is already there, intently staring at his screen. He takes the coffee she gives him with a grunt, then does a double take when he looks at her.

'You all right? You look like shit.'

'Thanks,' she grumbles. 'Couldn't sleep.'

He sits back in his chair. 'Everything okay?'

'Just the case.' She takes a sip of her coffee. 'And Josh.'

'He left with Mina. Not too happy with me.' He lowers his voice. 'You haven't spoken to him, I assume?'

'No.'

He nods slowly. 'It's the right decision, Freya.'

'I haven't said I'm not going to.'

'Oh. Okay.' He turns to his computer, his back to her.

Freya hasn't decided what to do. But she needs to do something. The gulf between Josh and her is widening, and she feels it more every day. Perhaps tonight will help, she tells herself. A few drinks, celebrations. New Year, new start. All that bollocks.

'I did a bit more digging into Sam Bowen,' Robin says, back to business. Freya feels her cheeks redden. She won't mention her little field trip last night; she didn't find out anything they didn't already know about Sam and Sara. And it would only give him another reason to be angry with her. 'He's a successful bloke. PhDs in everything, popular business as a therapist. Look how much he charges per hour.' He points to his screen. Sam Bowen's slick-looking website is up, showing eye-watering hourly fees. 'Plus, look at these testimonials. Apparently, these two are quite famous.'

Freya takes in the names and nods. 'Reality TV stars. They were on *Love Island*. Their break-up and subsequent marriage made the headlines.'

'Sounds like Dr Bowen was the reason for it. No wonder he can afford an R8.'

Freya takes a quick gasp of breath. 'That's it. The car.'

He looks at her, confused.

'It's like we were saying the other night: the body got from the pub into the hole somehow, right?' she says, excited. 'And… and…' She digs into her bag and grabs the folder of photographs. She flips through them quickly, then pulls one out, showing Robin. 'Here,' she says, triumphantly.

In the photo, the five of them stand next to a small car. It's a classic cream Mini Cooper, all of the men towering comically above it.

'Sam had a car,' Freya says. She leans over Robin, pointing to the number plate, just visible behind them.

'And if we find that car, we might find something that ties them to the body,' Robin finishes.

43

All it took was a wink for Sara to fall in love. A wink and a punch in the face.

Their second term of university, just after Christmas, and they had strayed from halls into Portswood for a night out. Juicy Lucys at Jesters, a revolting green toxic punch in even less salubrious surroundings. But the place was heaving.

Sara was drunk and happy. She was with her friends. It was a weekend with nothing but a long walk home and a bag of chips in her future. She leaned languorously against Alex as he told a story, one arm around her, the other holding his pint, gesturing dangerously. She'd long lost track of what they were actually discussing, but Sam was taking the piss, Mike laughing. Meg was jigging next to her, eyes half-closed, a beat in her head only she could hear. She opened her eyes and grabbed Sara's arm.

'Come with me to the loo,' she said.

The two of them weaved their way to the toilets, pushing past drunk girls and unwieldy men. At the back, the club was dark, disco lights flashing as music blasted out.

They made it to the shabby bathroom and waited in the queue. On the walls Steve announced his intentions to fuck Anna; a more philosophic scrawl told Sara to follow her dreams and cover her footsteps, a proclamation she found faintly sinister. Meg turned to her, a mischievous look in her eye.

'What do you think of Mike?' Meg asked.

'Mike who?' Then she twigged. 'Our Mike? He's…'

Stable, solid Mike. Who wrote in tiny block capitals. Who made sure the washing-up was done and everyone locked the door when they went out. 'I haven't thought of him in that way.'

'I think he likes you,' Meg replied with a raise of her eyebrows. A cubicle came free and she headed inside. 'Would you?' she shouted.

Would she? Probably not. It made Sara uneasy. Would a relationship between two of them upset the balance of their group? Her wonderful new friends who, even after just four months, Sara never wanted to be without.

But Meg's comment about Mike opened a new window of thought. Not Mike, but maybe someone else?

She'd been attracted to Sam from the beginning. His confidence, the floppy blond hair, the blue eyes. He didn't give a shit what anyone thought of him – a world view that Sara found intoxicating. But he'd never shown any interest in her. The opposite, in fact. He'd banter with Meg, winding her up. Deliberately refusing to put the glass bottles in the recycling, shoving his meat kebabs in her vegetarian face after nights out. She'd laugh, playfully hit him, push him away. But Sara? Sara, he ignored.

Sara and Meg left the toilets and then, with a squeal, Meg dragged her to the sticky dance floor. Cheesy hits blasted out of the speakers; people crammed into the tiny space. Something indescribable dripped from above. Sweat from hot, dancing bodies, condensation on the ceiling.

Christina Aguilera, Britney Spears, Five. All the hits were on that night. Sara and Meg threw themselves around, dancing wildly, their inhibitions dissipated in the darkness.

She noticed the smell first. Overdone aftershave mixed with old beer and testosterone. A group of men from the rugby club. They had their T-shirts off; their eyes were keen, smiles expectant. Locked onto their prey. They danced behind Sara and Meg, if you could call it that. More hands and fingers than rhythm.

Sara laughed and pushed them away. Nothing new if you were blonde and pretty. They were undeterred; Sara could see by the look on Meg's face that she was getting annoyed.

And then the shout.

'Oi!'

One of the rugby boys was on his arse, another squaring up to the three men behind them. Sara turned quickly. Sam, Mike and Alex were there. Eighteen years old, pigeon-chested in comparison, but shoulder to shoulder. Mike looked wary, Alex was annoyed. And Sam? Sam was standing chest to chest with the largest rugby bloke. He looked away from the man's furious gaze and met Sara's eye. He winked.

And then the right hook hit him squarely in the face.

–

They were thrown out. Of course they were. Starting fights, for whatever reason, wasn't something bouncers tolerated. The five of them linked arms and walked a few metres up the road, then collapsed on a park bench, laughing.

'Oh, you twats,' Meg cackled. 'What were you thinking? You couldn't take those guys.'

'We thought we'd try,' Alex said. 'Defend your honour, and all that.'

'It's not the fucking sixteenth century.'

Sara looked over to Sam. He was gingerly touching the skin around his left eye, wincing. Bruises were already starting to blossom, glorious in their red and black.

'We need to get you some ice,' she said to him.

He smiled. She felt that charge again, hormones racing. 'I'll live,' he said.

The others had started walking up the road towards home. Sara looked at them, waiting. She didn't want to join them; she wanted this moment. With him.

'You shouldn't have waded in like that,' she said. She moved closer to him, pretending to look at the shiner. 'You should have thought first.'

'Where would the fun be in that?'

Then he leaned up and kissed her. No hesitation. And with that, she fell in love.

–

In her empty house, she thinks about that night and the few years after. She never stopped loving Sam, so how had she ended up with Mike? The thing she loved about Sam – his spontaneity, his random nature, the quick, sometimes snippy comments – became his undoing. She needed stability, solidity. For someone to take the bins out. And look how that had ended.

Every now and then she'd google Dr Sam Bowen. She'd seen his flourishing career, the wedding announcements. Felt jealous about every one. Less fanfare around the divorces, but who could blame him. It wasn't good for business.

And then he'd called her. Out of nowhere.

'Can I see you?'

'Yes.'

No hesitation.

There he was. Like no time had passed. Like she was eighteen again. No worries, no kids. Carefree. A time she'd forgotten but yearned for. Hotel rooms, his flat, anywhere, just so they could be together.

But what now? It's New Year's Eve and he arrives, champagne in hand. But they don't celebrate, can't talk. They pick at food, watch television, bodies close. They go to bed. There's safety in the familiarity of his body, in the way he moves. In his soft murmur and the feel of his fingertips.

She can't imagine anyone else, not now she has him again.

But even as they fall asleep, early, before the chimes of the new year, she blames him. Why couldn't you have saved me? she thinks. Why couldn't you have saved me, then?

44

Robin flinches at the noise; it affects him physically, pressure from within. A rhythmic bassline, thumping on his diaphragm, coupled with chatter and shouting from hundreds of people shoved into a bar.

Robin hasn't been somewhere like this in years, and now he remembers why. Liam pushes through the throng, a hand in the air, waving to someone Robin can't even see. It baffles him how anyone can feel at home in this environment. Liam turns, sees Robin's expression and doubles back.

'Don't pull out on me now, you grumpy sod,' he shouts.

'It's not my thing, Liam,' Robin protests. 'I'll go. I don't want to ruin your night—'

'Don't you dare.' Liam moves behind him and physically pushes Robin towards the bar. He laughs, despite himself, then obeys, walking towards the one place that can at least provide him with alcohol.

Ten minutes later, he is marginally happier. They have pints in their hands and have climbed the flight of stairs to the top floor, where it's less crowded and they have a table. Liam introduces Robin: nods all round, smiles, a few faces he even recognises from nights out in the past with Georgia. He sips his beer, pensively.

The bar is part of a massive chain; there's nothing original about the decor. Cream walls, dark wooden tables and chairs. Nothing is made for comfort; it is all about profit margins and extracting money from punters as quickly as possible. Their table is up in a corner – a cushion built into an alcove, then high bar stools all round. Robin takes the one closest to the stairs, quietly planning his escape. One hour, maybe two? He doesn't need to stay until midnight. He could sneak away once Liam's pissed. Pick up some chips on the walk home. Be back in time to watch the fireworks on TV and maybe the end of the *Graham Norton* special.

A woman arrives, a few friends in tow. She's petite, wiry, with a long face and huge teeth that make her resemble a small pony. Liam smiles happily and goes over to greet her.

Robin's met her before: Lizzie, Liam's new girlfriend. At first, he found it hard to watch Liam with someone who wasn't Georgia, but he knows how happy she makes him and he doesn't want to begrudge him that. Also, he likes her.

She comes up to him and gives him a kiss on the cheek. 'I had a fiver on you not coming tonight,' she says with a laugh.

'The night's still young.'

She looks around the bar. 'I hope none of my students are here,' she says. 'That's all I need when I go back next week.'

She's a secondary school teacher, Year 10. 'The worst buggers you could hope to teach,' she told him when they first met. 'But I like a challenge.'

He's aware of glances from a few of her friends and smiles awkwardly. He wonders what Lizzie has told them;

what sound bites would sum him up. Cop, detective. Liam's brother-in-law. Family. Never married. No kids. He doesn't sound too bad when put like that. He mentally adds a few of his own. Workaholic. Depressive. Avoidant. Makes morally dubious decisions.

He's so not in the mood for this. He takes his phone out of his pocket and looks at it, willing a message to appear on the screen.

'Where's Freya tonight?' Liam asks, reading his mind.

He puts his phone away with a scowl. 'Out.'

'In town? Shall we see if we can meet her later?'

Robin shakes his head. 'Nah. She's with him. SuperTed.'

Liam takes a sip of his pint. 'What's so wrong with this guy, anyway? From what you've told me he seems okay. Good at his job, nice to Freya?'

'He's just so bloody...' Robin struggles to put into words why Josh Smith annoys him so much. 'Perfect.'

'Is that really it?'

'What do you mean?'

'Well...' Liam tilts his head to one side. 'Is it that you don't like Freya going out with this bloke in particular, or...?'

Robin doesn't like where this is going. 'Or?'

Liam laughs. 'Come on, you're not this stupid, Robin.' Lizzie comes over, putting her arms round Liam's middle.

'What are we talking about?' she asks.

'Robin's continued hatred for Freya's boyfriend.' He bends down and plants a kiss on her forehead.

'Oh, yes, him. He's handsome. She showed me a photo.'

Robin screws up his face.

'Oh...' Lizzie says. 'Is that it?'

'Exactly,' Liam replies.

'Do I need to be here?' Robin says, mock stroppy. He finishes the last inch of beer in his glass. 'Shall I leave you two alone to talk about me? Let me know what you decide when I get back.'

He plonks his pint glass on the table and heads towards the bar. It's busy, and he joins the jostling queue.

Of course, he knows what Liam is getting at. Liam's had his theory, from the beginning, that something's going on between Freya and Robin. Something more than friends. Robin's always denied it, but it's hard to keep pushing it to one side given his strength of feeling about Josh. And now he and Freya aren't getting on that well, he's felt her absence. When he sees something funny, he wants to message her about it. When there's an item on the news, he wants to ask her opinion, hear her babble on, forming coherent arguments out of the stream of consciousness pouring from her mouth.

They'd got through another day together. Stuttered conversations, sharing information when they had to. Freya's brainwave about Sam Bowen's old car had come up trumps. Even though the Mini must be ancient by now, it had been bought by a man called Bert Moss, a classic car dealer in Oxford. He confirmed he had it, agreeing to meet them the next day.

'But it's New Year!' Freya protested. 'Give me one day off, at least.'

But the man is going on holiday after that, so this is their only chance.

'I'll go alone, don't worry.'

'No, no. I'll come. Just make it after lunch, at least. Please.'

So the time was confirmed for two p.m. Robin isn't sure how spending a few hours in the car with Freya is going to go.

He's only one row of people from the bar now. There's a woman in front of him, ordering what seems to be a lengthy list of drinks. He waits patiently, his body pressed against hers in the bustle. She smells nice, of shampoo and perfume.

And then she turns.

'Detective Sergeant Robin Butler!'

He blinks. The woman smiles. He doesn't recognise her, he doesn't. They move round each other awkwardly, Robin taking her place next to the bar, the woman carrying three drinks in her hands, spilling them slightly on his shoes. The barman gets bored of waiting and moves on to the next guy.

'Wait a sec,' she says. 'I'll get rid of these. I'll come back.'

He watches her go, desperately trying to place her in his memory. She has long brown wavy hair, curling slightly on her shoulders. Big smile. She clearly knows him from work. Someone he's interviewed?

'Two bottles of Corona and a G and T, please, mate,' Robin says as the barman's attention moves back to him.

An old colleague? From training?

He pays and pushes his way out. He looks around for her; she's standing to one side, watching him. And then he realises.

He walks over, smiling. 'DI Craig,' he says.

'Jo, please. And I didn't think you'd recognised me.'

'It took a while,' he confesses. 'You look different.' Nicer, he thinks, but doesn't say. 'What are you doing here? I thought you lived in Reading.'

'I do. I'm visiting friends.' She points to a group of women on the far side, all in sparkly tops and jeans. They stare at him. 'And this is your home turf?'

'Yes, absolutely.'

Liam appears beside him, taking two of the drinks out of his hands.

'Hello,' he says, unperturbed by Robin's silence. 'I'm Liam. And you are?'

'Sorry,' Robin stutters. 'This is Jo Craig. She was the senior officer in charge of Finn's case in June.' He points to Liam. 'This guy is the reason for me being out tonight. My brother-in-law.'

'I didn't know you were married,' Jo says.

'He's not,' Liam interjects quickly. 'I was married to his sister.' He puts his arms round Robin's shoulders. 'Free as a bird, aren't you, Robbie?'

'Piss off, Liam.'

Liam laughs and goes back to the table.

'Sorry about him, he's a bit drunk,' Robin says.

'Aren't we all?' she replies, and he notices her cheeks are flushed, her eyes bright. 'How is Finn doing?'

'He's good. Making small steps. I mean,' Robin shrugs, 'he's never going to be back to normal, but he's making progress. Little things, like remembering what he did that day, what he ate for lunch.'

'That's good,' she echoes.

They stand in silence, each taking a sip from their drinks.

'It's nice to bump into you like this,' she says, at last. 'Last time we met I spent most of my time shouting at you.'

Robin laughs. 'You did. Although I deserved it.'

'You definitely deserved it. You were such a pain in my arse. But I was glad you were there.'

'Really?'

'Yes. We got the right result. If it hadn't been for you, pushing, we might not have got there in the end.'

'Shoving, more like. As subtle as a freight train.'

She laughs and puts a hand on his arm. She's unmistakably flirting, and he doesn't know how to respond.

'Would you like to join us?' he asks. He points to his group of friends on the far side. 'We even have a table.'

'A precious commodity indeed,' she laughs. She looks up at him with a smile. 'I'm sure we'd love to.'

45

Freya is drunk. Not a bit tipsy, or wobbling slightly, but full-on, fancy-a-nap, not-sure-which-way-is-up hammered. She puts her chin on her hands on the table then rests her glass against her lips. The smell of alcohol makes her feel slightly sick.

'Hey, Freya.' A large bloke sits down next to her. Adam – Josh's mate from football. 'How are you doing?'

'I'm pissed.'

'I can tell. Where's Josh?'

She doesn't lift her head, but points a wobbly finger towards the bar. 'Gone to get some water.'

'Glad to hear it. You're sound, you know that, Freya?'

'Hmm?'

'Because when Josh said you and him were together, I thought, well, thank fuck. Because the last thing he needed was some stuck-up bitch like Elise again.'

'Thanks, Adam,' she slurs. 'Good to know.'

'And you're lovely.' He places a heavy paw on Freya's shoulder. She tilts slightly.

'Where's your wife tonight?'

'Home. With the kiddies. I'm kipping on Josh's floor.'

This is news to Freya. Josh has Adam to stay. With a flash of insecurity, Freya wonders whether that means he isn't going to stay at hers. Had he planned to sleep at his own place? What did that step backward mean for their relationship?

Adam continues: 'She won't let me back in when I've been drinking.'

'Sensible woman.'

He nods, his face serious. 'Love of my life, that lady.'

'Leave Freya alone, Adam,' Josh says, returning. He puts a pint of water in front of Freya. 'Drink that,' he instructs.

She peels her face off the sticky table, then tips the glass towards her mouth, spilling some on her top. 'Sorry,' she slurs.

'You're fine.' He sighs then smiles sympathetically. 'How about I take you home?'

'No, no, I don't want to ruin your night. We can stay.'

He laughs softly. 'Come on, you alcoholic. Let's go.'

He pulls Freya to her feet; she sways as he puts his arm around her. Adam looks up, questioning.

'Key's in the lockbox,' Josh comments. Adam gives a thumbs up and turns back to his pint.

They wobble out of the pub and down the road.

'I'm sorry, Josh,' Freya burbles as they go. 'I didn't mean to ruin your evening. It's not even midnight—'

'Not even close,' Josh mutters.

'I just can't take my drink anymore. And with everything that's been going on, I wanted us to have some fun, but I got it wrong, and now you're angry with me.'

'I'm not angry with you.'

'You are. You are.' Freya starts to cry. 'And now you're going to dump me and that'll be it and you're the best boyfriend, and so nice to me, and...'

Josh stops, and Freya collapses slowly to the pavement. She crouches on the concrete, legs crossed, head against her knees, staring at the cigarette butts in the gutter through self-indulgent tears.

Freya's aware she's being pathetic. And this part of her – this insecure, needy wimp – is not something she's proud of. But the alcohol has destroyed all semblance of the confident woman she normally is. Her defences are down, and it's not pretty.

'Freya,' Josh says softly. He sits down next to her, then reaches across and does the buttons up on her coat. 'I'm not angry with you.'

'You are—'

'I'm not. I know things have been odd between us, but it's only because I want to be with you. I want you to share your life with me. And I feel like you've been shutting me out.'

Freya nods, slowly. She's not being honest with Josh, but how can she? She doesn't want to break Robin's trust, but she can't lie, either.

'I'm sorry, Josh,' she says. She sniffs back her snotty nose. 'I'll make it up to you.'

'You will.' He gives her a big grin. 'Maybe tomorrow.'

Freya wails and starts crying again. 'I have to work tomorrow. I'm going to Oxford with Robin to find this car.'

'Right.' Josh is quiet again, but he puts his arm around Freya. She leans into him. 'Robin,' he says quietly to himself. 'Why do you get to call him by his first name when I get shouted at for anything less than DS Butler?'

'Because we're friends. No.' She shakes her head. Everything seems blurry right now to Freya. Sentences won't form. Thoughts won't take shape. 'No, not friends,' she says, then shuts up, realising she's strayed into dangerous territory. The relationship between her and

Robin is hard to define and she's not going to try now. Not to Josh. And certainly not when she's as drunk as she is.

She rests her head on Josh's shoulder and closes her eyes. 'I'll sleep here tonight,' she says, drowsily.

Josh sighs, then moves her gently, getting to his feet. He holds out his hands and pulls Freya up to standing.

'Come on,' he says, wearily. 'Let's take you home.'

46

Quarter of an hour until midnight, and Robin has to admit he's enjoying himself. The music has changed from the interminable drum and bass to songs he recognises, his level of drunkenness is at the optimal point where everything is amusing, and the company? Well. The company is… unexpected.

Jo Craig has dragged her friends over, a group of women pleased to share the evening with Liam's cycling and triathlon buddies. Men with rugged beards and rippling six-packs, who can manage four pints and still get up for a swim in the sea the next morning. There is laughter and flirting. In one corner, two people are sucking each other's faces with a level of intensity normally seen only in teenagers.

'She's just got divorced,' Jo says, noticing Robin's disbelieving expression.

'That explains it.' He turns his attention back to her. His good mood is making him bold. 'What about you, Jo? Are you seeing anyone?'

'Me? No. There was someone, and I thought it could be something, but we split up about six months ago. Around the time we met.' She laughs. 'That's my excuse for my horrible mood then, anyway.'

'You were fine. You were doing your job.'

'I wasn't. Not well, anyway. And then you came along, all smouldering frowns—'

He snorts. 'I wasn't smouldering!'

'You were. But don't worry. It's a look that suits you.'

He lowers his brow and looks at her, mocking.

'Not like that!' She laughs. 'You're nicer this way. I like this version more.'

Her compliment stuns him into silence. Women aren't normally this friendly with him. Keen. She meets his gaze and leans in slightly. Is she…? Does she want him to kiss her? Shit. What should he do? Should he…? He would really like to.

Then there's commotion around him, and the moment is lost. A glass of champagne is thrust into his hands and people shout out the countdown. Jo is next to him, chanting along.

Three, two, one.

Happy New Year.

A series of loud bangs as party poppers are released into the air. He laughs, glitter and streamers flying. Liam appears and gives him a big hug. The whole pub is a mass of commotion and noise, and he looks around, taking it all in.

Another year. He's survived another year.

He feels a hand in his and sees Jo next to him. She removes a streamer from his shoulder with a smile.

'Happy New Year, Robin,' she says.

And she leans up and kisses him.

47

Mike hears the muted celebrations from the nurses' station at midnight. The whispers of 'Happy New Year' and the chink of soft drinks in plastic glasses. A nurse comes by and checks his obs, giving him a broad smile that he doesn't return.

He turns his head away as she attaches the blood pressure cuff, then checks his breathing. Oxygen saturation and heart rate are measured via the probe on the one remaining healthy finger, the nurse gently manoeuvring round the damaged ones.

He wonders what Sara's doing, whether she's with *him*, his teeth gritting in anger. He remembers their time at university when she was with Sam. The paper-thin walls and the noises that couldn't be disguised. It was often a source of amusement in the morning for the household; something he doesn't find funny now.

What does the future have in store for him? Before, he'd planned to move in with Alex, albeit temporarily, while he found his feet, but now where can he go? His only option is home, when the doctors let him. Will Sara stay? Will she move in with Sam? She can't possibly take the kids *there*, surely?

Meg updated him on the case yesterday. At least, as much as she knew, which wasn't a lot. He's cut off in here, the lack of access to the news or his phone intensifying his frustration and worry. He got the sense she wasn't telling him something. Hesitation in her body language, refusal to make eye contact. He couldn't extract any more before the nurse asked her to leave, Meg placing a kiss on his cheek that lingered a little too long for his liking.

He's always told himself: keep quiet. As an ex-copper, he knows how hard some crimes are to prove; start to talk and you'll be putty in their hands. But now, as loneliness creeps in at the edges, as anger and bitterness swell, it's only a matter of time. Before that resolution breaks, and all will be revealed.

48

Saturday

Oh. Fuck. Ugh.

Freya is incapable of forming complete sentences. Her head thumps, her mouth is dry and the less said about her stomach, the better.

She lies motionless on the bed; even her breathing makes her nauseous.

'Morning, sunshine.'

She doesn't dare lift her head. 'How are you so cheerful?' she mutters.

'You drank all the alcohol before I had a chance to,' Josh says. He drops down on the bed. The mattress rocks in a dangerous manner. 'Never felt so good on New Year's Day.'

'You're welcome,' Freya replies. She groans, trying to push herself up. Her head spins but she persists, resting back on the pillows. Josh hands her a pint of water and she sips it, gratefully.

'I am so sorry,' she says.

Josh waves her apology away. 'It's fine. It made a nice change. It's usually you dragging me home after the pub.'

'But last night…' She squeezes her eyes shut again. 'Was I awful?'

'You were sick. But in a bush on the way home, so nothing to clear up here.'

Freya runs her tongue round her teeth. Furry.

'And you were waffling away like a crazy person.'

Freya freezes. 'I was? About what?'

'Something to do with a guy called Sam?'

'The murder. One of the victims found on the beach.'

'Okay. Well, him.' He pauses. 'And you said something about Jon.'

'What did I say?'

Josh pauses, and Freya fears the worst. 'That you missed him,' he says quietly. 'And then you started talking about Butler and I lost track.'

'I'm sorry,' Freya repeats.

'It's okay. It's right that you miss him. You two were in love, I assume?'

Freya nods. It's too much of an effort this morning to resist Josh's questions.

'How long were you together?'

'Not long. Just over a year.'

'How did he die?'

'He…' Freya pauses. She doesn't want to lie. But to tell the truth? Now? There's no way it's the right time. 'We thought it was an accident.'

Josh looks confused. 'Thought? What happened?'

'It's complicated.' Freya can't think straight. She puts a hand to her head, taking some relief from the cold against her hot forehead. 'I don't want to talk about how he died. It wasn't a good time.'

Josh's face clouds. 'Okay, yes, sure.' He leans back on the bed next to her. 'Then tell me something about him. What was he like?'

Freya pauses. She thinks about Jon. How different he was to Josh. She smiles softly. 'He was always untidy. Always scruffy. He had messy blond hair that never sat straight. It was always sticking up at the sides.'

'Did you live together?'

'No, he…' *lived with his wife*. 'Had his own place. But we talked about it. We would have liked to.'

She leans into Josh's chest, feeling his arm go round her. For the first time in days, she thinks this might be okay. Spare a few details, discuss the easy stuff.

And talking about Jon has been nice. None of her friends had met him. Robin only knew him as a man who'd been murdered. She can remember how he was, to her. Quiet. Self-sacrificing. Taking everything that life threw at him and carrying on regardless. He was a solid presence by her side, the person she came to depend on.

And now she realises the similarities, between Jonathan and Robin. Jon had left her life precisely the day that Robin arrived. They were similar men: insular, stoic. Men who had dealt with the worst that life had to offer and had carried on without complaint. But before she can analyse that train of thought further, Josh distracts her.

'The owner of my place got in touch the other week,' he says. 'He's looking to sell.'

'He's going to throw you out?'

Josh smiles. 'Me and the other three. But it's about time, don't you think, Freya? I can't live in a shithole forever.'

She shifts slightly, looking up at him.

'I still have my flat in Newcastle. The guy renting it has mentioned he'd like to buy it. I could sell. Get somewhere down here.'

Freya feels that uncertainty again. She's not sure what he's getting at. 'What would you look for?'

'I don't know. A few bedrooms. A garden.' He pauses. 'Of course,' he says, 'if you sold your house and we bought together, we could afford somewhere really nice.'

She looks up; he's smiling. 'We could do that,' she says, returning his grin. 'If that's what you want.'

'I want that very much, Freya,' he says, and he leans down to kiss her. Then he frowns. 'Now, if you could just clean your teeth, then I wouldn't have to snog a girlfriend who smells of puke.'

'Oh, no,' Freya squeals, and rushes off to the bathroom.

49

Robin's been thinking about Jo all morning. They spent hours in the bar talking, until the place closed at two a.m. He left her with her friends, after sharing a final kiss.

'You still have my number?' she asked. He nodded. 'Then call me.'

He walked home with a spring in his step. And now, this afternoon, for the first time in a while, he feels good.

He laughs when he sees Freya. She's standing outside her house, coat buttoned up to her nose, eyes almost closed.

'It's not funny,' she grumbles as she gets into the car. 'Drive slowly and gently.'

'What did you drink?'

'Wine. All the wine.'

And he tries, he really does. But he can't resist taking a few corners a little too quickly, braking hard when he doesn't need to. She glares, sipping slowly at her water bottle.

'Quit it, Butler,' she growls. 'Unless you want a puddle of vom in your footwell.' He snorts, putting his foot down hard as they go round another corner. 'And what's got you in such a sunny mood?'

'Had a good night. How was yours? Were you with Josh?'

She looks at him. 'Yes.'

'Did you—'

'No.' She sighs. 'We talked a bit this morning, though. About Jon and what he was like.'

'Okay.' Robin negotiates a junction off the A34 towards Oxford.

'And it was nice. Not to have to lie.'

He doesn't comment. He doesn't want a fight, not now. Work comes first.

'Do you remember what that was like, back then?' she continues. 'That October. When you told me everything that happened to you?'

Robin swallows. Yes, he does. Confessing to Freya had been cathartic, a release of everything he had bottled up for so long.

'But in October last year,' he begins, 'I had reached a point where everything was so terrible that telling you – and the consequences of it all – couldn't possibly have made anything worse.' He keeps his eyes fixed on the road; he's aware she's turned slightly in her seat, watching him. 'I was prepared to go to jail. Take whatever came my way. Because the alternative – living another day alone, depressed, wanting to die – was the lowest I could go. But you.' He glances across to Freya. Despite her hangover, he's struck by how lovely she is and how much he cares about her. 'You have everything ahead of you. A good job, probably promotions and a long career. Love, marriage, kids. Don't risk all that in a mistaken belief that the truth is the best way forward.'

The car is silent. He glances across. Freya has turned and is looking out of the window to her left, her hand raised to her mouth. She sniffs, and Robin wonders if she's crying. He stays quiet. He has no idea what to do if she is.

–

He obeys the satnav and they arrive in the suburbs of Oxford, at an industrial estate. Grey corrugated boxes line up alongside chain metal fences; Robin follows the road round to the end.

It's clear they're in the right place. Multiple cars in varying states of repair, all shapes and sizes, stacked up like Tetris. Some have parts missing, cannibalised for the shiny, completed vehicles in front. There's a large building behind, its huge, shuttered doors half-open.

Robin pats the steering wheel reassuringly. 'We'll be back, I promise,' he says to his old Volvo, and he hears Freya laugh softly. It's not much, but it's something.

A man comes out to greet them, wiping his hands on an oily rag.

'Detective Butler?' he asks, and Robin nods. 'Bert Moss. We spoke on the phone.'

'This is DC West,' he says, introducing Freya.

'I would shake your hands, but…' He shows them his dirty palms. 'Coffee, tea? You can always make it yourself?'

Robin smiles. 'Yes, we'll do that, thank you.'

They walk into the main garage, their eyes adjusting to the dim light as they go inside. There's a classic car raised up on the lift above them, a bright light shining into its innards.

'A 1972 MGB Roadster,' Bert says. 'V8. Nasty case of rust. Been kept at the beach.' He tuts. 'Sea air. Does it every time.' He points to the mugs and kettle resting on a tray over a fridge. 'Help yourself.'

Robin goes over and puts the kettle on, leaving Freya peering at another vehicle.

'Alfa Romeo Spider,' he hears her say, and the man agrees. 'My grandad had one of these.'

'Then he was a lucky man. This one was a wreck when it came in. It's taken me the best part of a year to do it up. Are you interested?'

'Don't tempt me.'

'I can see you in it,' Bert continues, and Robin wonders if the old man is flirting. 'Just the car for a woman like you. Cool, quick, ready for anything. You can tell a lot about a person by the car they drive.'

Robin pours water into the mugs. He glances back, and Bert is appraising his V60.

'That must be your car, Detective. I'm guessing not an official police vehicle.'

'And you'd be right,' Robin agrees. 'Go on then, what does that tell you?' He walks back to join them and hands a mug of coffee to Freya.

The man grins. 'Solid. Dependable. Puts his faith in things he knows.' He pauses. 'Safety above all else.'

'All that from a Volvo,' Freya says. 'Remarkable.' She smiles at Robin, and he feels a bond. A connection, with everything that's passed between them.

The man laughs. 'Some people have their tea leaves. I have my cars. Anyway, that old Mini. It's out the back.'

He walks through the garage and they follow him to the concrete yard behind. Here are even more cars. Some without doors, others a mismatch of different pieces. Bert pulls at a tarpaulin and a cream Mini is revealed. It's the classic design: two doors, boot at the back. It's tiny. Robin had forgotten how small these old things were.

'Mini Cooper, 1988. I got her about ten years ago but have only just started work on the restoration. New doors, new engine.'

Robin peers inside. 'And we're sure this is the same one?' he says, pointing to the space at the front where the plates should be.

'Yeah, absolutely.' He takes a key out of his pocket and goes round to the small silver handle on the boot. He turns it and it drops down, showing two old metal number plates. 'F472 TRU. That your car?'

'Yeah,' Robin says, distracted. He's appraising the tiny boot, then looks up at Freya. 'What do you think?' he asks.

'No way you could get a body in there,' she agrees.

Bert looks between the two of them. 'That's why you want the car?'

'We believe it was used to transport a murder victim twenty years ago,' Robin replies.

The man tilts his head to one side. 'Were they tall? Because if not, you could get them in the back seat.'

Robin crouches down and looks through the window, his hands cupped against the glass. It could work, he's right. 'Are those the original seats?' he asks and the man nods.

'Yes, but the upholstery's been stripped. She arrived like that,' he says. Then his face looks downcast. 'You're going to want to take her, aren't you?'

'I'm sorry,' Robin says. 'You'll get it back. But right now, this car is our best chance at proving who murdered a man twenty years ago.'

Robin looks back through the window. The seat covers have gone, bare plastic looking back. But hair, blood, skin. They get everywhere. Tiny cells of evidence.

If the body was there, then they'll be there, too. Still. After all this time.

50

They cordon off the car, Robin calls Thames Valley Police to request a scene guard; Freya phones Jess to arrange collection. The Crime Scene Manager is mildly miffed when she finally answers the phone.

'You want me to send a truck on New Year's Day to Oxford?' she says to Freya. 'Do you know how bad my hangover is right now?'

'Much like mine,' Freya replies dully, the painkillers starting to wear off. Her stomach has gone from feeling like she would never eat again to ravenously hungry.

'This is the punishment we get for having fun, Freya,' she says. She confirms she'll get it sorted and hangs up. Freya stuffs her phone in her pocket and walks over to where Robin is talking to Bert.

'Done?' he asks.

'Jess will get the truck over today.'

He nods, seemingly satisfied with her response.

'Now,' Freya says, forcing a smile on her face. 'Can we get something to eat, please?'

They follow Bert's directions to the local café down the road. They walk in silence, scarves pulled up to their chins, hats low on their heads. The snow is no longer threatening but the meteorologists talked about freezing temperatures, black ice. Freya feels thankful for Robin's faithful Volvo, damaged bumper notwithstanding.

He holds the door open when they get there. It's a simple place. Cheap plastic tables, laminated menus, small tumblers that remind Freya of school canteens. But it's buzzing with people, the windows steamed with condensation. The friendly waitress points them to a table at the front of the café and they sit down.

Freya pulls her coat off as the heat from the café makes itself known; Robin meets her eyes and smiles quickly. His old smile. The one she always thought held a thousand secrets, hiding the misery and the pain. It worries her that it's returned.

They direct their attention to their menus; the waitress comes over and they order coffees.

'Can I have a pint of water as well, please?' Freya says and Robin snorts.

'What happened last night?' he asks again.

'I don't know,' she groans into her hands. 'I was nervous, and things haven't been going well with Josh lately—'

'They haven't?' Robin's surprised. 'I thought all was wonderful with Dogtanian?'

She ignores the insult, glad he's taking the piss again. 'It was,' she says. 'No, no, it is. It's… this whole thing with Jon.' She shrugs. 'Let's not talk about it now. How was your night? Did you go out?'

'I did. With Liam.'

'The whole night? You didn't sneak off before midnight for chips and a long walk home?'

He smiles. 'I considered it. But I got talking to some people and…' She senses he's holding something back but doesn't press him on it. 'I ended up staying. Even enjoyed myself.'

'Well!' She recoils with mock horror. 'Wonders will never cease.'

The waitress returns with their drinks: steaming hot coffee in chipped white mugs. Freya's pint of water. They both order bacon sandwiches.

'How did it go with Steph the other night?' Freya asks after downing half her water.

'I told you about the PM.'

'I meant… other things.' She raises her eyebrows suggestively.

'We're just friends, Steph and I. Nothing's going on.'

'Ah, pity. So nothing happened?' He pauses, and she catches his expression. 'I knew it! And?'

'And nothing. She's seeing someone. So, no more… you know.'

'Extracurricular activity?'

'Exactly.'

The bacon sandwiches arrive and Freya's glad of the distraction. In the past she's always felt okay discussing stuff like this with Robin, but for the last few months something has changed. His teasing about Josh, the silly names. They don't feel so innocent, more… jealous? But that's ridiculous. This is Robin.

He's odd, she knows that, but she always thought that she understood him. Under his frequently gruff manner is just a man who's not quite sure about his place in the world. His confidence at work isn't replicated in his personal life. He has few friends, not many people he would call family. And of all the people he knows, she's probably the closest to him.

But he doesn't think about her like that. She knows that for sure.

'Frey?'

'Hmm?' She hasn't been listening and he's looking at her, curious.

'You were staring at me funny.'

'Was I? Sorry. Just tired, I guess. Were you talking about the case?'

'Yeah. What we should do if the car comes up a blank.' He sighs. 'Wait for the lab and hope they have something on the lino?'

'What about the knife?' She pauses, wiping a smudge of ketchup from the plate with her finger and putting it in her mouth. 'If they've got any sense, they would have dumped it, right?'

'Exactly. And twenty years ago, it could be anywhere.'

'We could put out another public appeal?'

He pulls a face. 'I think we've exhausted that route. Plus, the uniforms and Josh and Mina have already done a house-to-house and have come up with nothing. You done?' He points to her plate and the last corner of her sandwich.

She nods. Robin gets up, picking the last bit of bacon from her plate and eating it.

'So, what?' he says before he leaves to pay the bill. 'We stare at them accusingly for a bit, and hope they crack?'

Freya watches him, feeling her hangover fading after the influx of carbs and caffeine. No more drinking, she chastises herself. Especially with the way things are at the moment. Who knows what she might say by mistake.

Robin returns, holding a bar of Dairy Milk that he bought from next to the till.

'Sugar,' he says as he puts it in front of her. 'To complete your restoration to full health.'

She smiles and follows him out of the café, enjoying the familiarity between them returning. Then she has a thought.

'What if we do exactly that?' she remarks. Robin looks at her blankly. 'I don't mean the staring part. Let's assume one of them did kill this guy. We don't know why, or who, but assuming something happened, they've lived with it for twenty years. It's a long time.' Robin's quiet and Freya knows he's thinking about the events of just over a year ago; everything she wants to tell Josh about. She carries on, her voice quieter. 'It's a lot to play on your mind.'

He nods. They walk, their hands pushed hard into their pockets, their faces to the ground.

'We need something to split them apart,' Robin says, after a moment. 'To make them doubt their loyalty to the group.'

'But how would we know?' Freya replies.

'We have their mobile numbers from Alex's phone. We track their activity. Watch, see what happens.'

'We don't have a warrant for that.'

'We don't need the evidence to be admissible. Let's see where it takes us. One of them might slip up.'

'So what do we do? How will we spook them?'

Robin turns to her with a grin. She knows that look, and it doesn't bode well.

'Leave that to me,' he says.

51

The rest of the way back they discuss the case. Throwing ideas to and fro, everything they know about The Five. Robin feels back on an even keel with Freya; this is what they do best, an exchange of ideas, minds pinging off each other.

They move on to other things; he drives while she talks. He's not really listening; she doesn't need particip-ation to the conversation. He likes that about her: her animation, her ability to fill dead air with anything that catches her interest. A contrast to him; a man who can't even string a sentence together some days, who creates awkward silences in social situations just by existing.

She's so suited to Josh, he thinks. As much as he hates to admit it, the man is charming and witty. Everything Robin isn't. But last night, with a bit of alcohol washing round his bloodstream, Robin felt like he managed to hold his own. And Jo told him to call her. Perhaps he will. Or perhaps he should leave last night as a good memory. A rare fragment in time where someone had liked him; a recollection to preserve rather than ruin with a terrible date.

With Freya it's always been different. There was no getting to know each other: they went from nothing to a forced intimacy within days, a closeness forged from shared disaster. Even though that time was terrible, he likes that they have that between them, that he knows more about her than a boyfriend ever would.

When she'd mentioned the problems with Josh, he'd felt a strange thrill. Not because he wanted her miserable, but… something. A suggestion of possibility. Ever since their trip away to Devon back in June, he's felt differently towards her. He's not sure what; he doesn't dare put a label on it.

He turns off the M3 towards Winchester. Freya's story has ended with little resolution or punchline; he doesn't think that matters. To him or to Freya.

'So, tomorrow?' Robin confirms and Freya nods.

'I'll text you when I'm there,' she says, sighing. She rests her head back in the seat as Robin makes the final turn to her house. 'I can't wait to get in. Lie on the sofa for the rest of the day.'

'Sounds like a plan. Do you want company? We could finish *Line of Duty*?'

There's an awkward pause and Robin regrets his sudden confidence.

'Josh is there,' Freya says at last.

'Okay.'

'Do you want to come in for coffee—'

'No. No, I'll head home. Might go for a run.'

'You crazy man. In this weather.' But the remark feels forced. The good mood evaporated with the mention of Josh.

He pulls up outside her house. She takes her seat belt off then stops, her fingers on the handle.

'I'm going to tell him,' she says softly.

At first Robin thinks he hasn't heard her correctly. But then she turns towards him and her face confirms it. Her mouth is downturned, her eyes on the edge of tears.

'No, Freya. You can't.'

'I have to.'

'Why?' he says, louder than he intended. 'Why, Freya? He'll go to Baker, or to Professional Standards, or worse. You'll be suspended. Fired, even. Please, Freya.'

'He won't.'

'How do you know?'

'I don't. But it's a risk I have to take. If we're going to have any sort of future together—'

'If you tell him, you won't have a future.'

'I love him, Robin.'

'You…' He feels a sting. But what did he expect? She's been with him for six months, they spend all their time together. Of course she's in love. But hearing it, said out loud, makes him feel strange. Rejected, from a party he was never invited to in the first place.

She's looking out of the windscreen now, towards her front door. He follows her gaze. It's opened while they've been talking and Josh is standing there, watching them, a puzzled expression on his face. He looks so bloody perfect, wearing jeans and a Superdry sweatshirt. Trendy, relaxed, cool. Robin's heard the rumours around the station. Josh with various women. And even though there's been nothing in the time he's been with Freya, Robin doesn't trust him. Someone like that, so charming, so fucking attractive. It's only a matter of time.

Robin feels the anger build. That Josh-bloody-Smith could hold her entire future in his hands.

'I'm sorry, Robin,' she says again. So trusting, so exposed. So ready to destroy everything for this man.

'Everything all right?' Josh shouts from the doorway. Fuck off, Robin thinks. *Fuck. Off.*

Instead, Robin turns to Freya, directing all his anger her way. 'Him?' he hisses, with an angry jab in his direction. 'That twat? You'd risk it all, for him?'

But Freya doesn't reply. She bites her lip, her face turned down, then gets out of the car. The door bangs and she walks quickly away.

He doesn't watch her go. He puts the car into gear and guns it away from her house. He speeds back, slamming the front door when he gets home. He puts on his running gear, pumping the loudest music possible through his headphones as he runs out across the freezing concrete. His lungs burn, his fingers turn to blocks of ice, but he carries on, taking his frustration out on the tarmac.

It's not until he's two miles out that he realises the reason for his anger. He's upset. He feels like he's been pushed to the side, rejected by the one person he cares for the most.

Freya had to decide: tell Josh and risk him reporting her. Risk him finding out exactly what happened all those months ago with Jonathan and Amy Miller. Risk him discovering what Freya had found when she looked into Robin's sister's case.

She had to choose. Between him and Josh. Even though Robin knows it was inevitable, she'd put Josh first. And that's the thing that hurts.

52

Freya dips her head, forcing back tears as Josh walks over.

'What was that?' he says, glancing towards Robin's car as it drives away.

'It was nothing.'

'It looked like you were arguing. What about?'

She pushes past him into the house. 'It's nothing,' she repeats.

He follows her, watching closely as she takes off her coat and scarf. 'Is he giving you a hard time about the case? Because you haven't made any progress? That's not on. As the senior officer, it's his responsibility, not yours. And it's your day off. You are doing the best you can.' Josh's eyes are flaring with anger. He stops, waiting for a response. 'Seriously, Freya. Complain to Baker. I'll back you up.'

'No, no, it's not...' She starts to walk away into the kitchen, but he follows.

'Is it to do with me? Has he got a problem with us?'

'Leave it, Josh.'

'That's none of his business. We've followed protocol. Nobody else has a problem with us being together.'

'It's not to do with you.'

'It is. I saw him point at me. What right does he have to take it out on you? What a dickhead. I'll have it out with him. I'll—'

'Leave it, Josh!' She shouts this time, tired and overemotional in the face of his ranting. He quietens, stunned by her exclamation. 'Look, it's personal. Okay? Between me and Robin.'

He frowns. 'What's so personal you can't tell your boyfriend?'

'He… I… Please leave it.'

'Are you cheating on me with Butler?'

'No!'

'So what is it?'

She screws her eyes shut. She was so sure in the car, so certain that telling Josh was the right thing. But now, in the face of his fury, she has doubts again. She's angry with Robin, upset by his dismissal of her, but maybe he has a point. Can she risk her whole life for this man?

Josh is staring at her, confusion and bitterness across his face.

'I'm sorry, Josh. I would like to tell you, but I can't.'

'Even after everything I said the other night? This is one more, isn't it? In the long list of things you won't tell me about.' He stares at Freya, expecting her to crack. But she can't. She can't.

Everything Robin has said – he's right. Not the inconsiderate, male-ego-raging way he'd said it, but the gist of his argument. She doesn't know how Josh will react. She'd be devastated if she lost her job, or – if the worst happened – Robin was investigated, too. But yet… but yet. Josh knows something's up, and he won't let it go.

'I'm sorry, Josh.' She starts to walk away, but he catches her hand.

'Just tell me one thing,' he says.

She waits.

'Is there anything going on between you and Robin?'

'No.' She can be truthful about that, at least. 'Absolutely not.'

'Does he want there to be?'

'No.'

'Was there?'

She frowns. 'What do you mean?'

'Has anything ever happened between you and Butler?'

She goes to say no. She even opens her mouth, but then she stops. It's an almost imperceptible pause, but Josh notices it.

'There was?' His voice rises into a squeak. 'What? When?'

'No, Josh. It was nothing. Over a year ago. When we first started working together.' His eyes are open wide with disbelief. 'We were... I don't know. We kissed. Once. That was it. We both knew it was a mistake.'

'Were you drunk?'

'No. No, we weren't.' She remembers that strange kiss. The fumble of hands on skin, clothes removed. Being that close to Robin. It feels strange now, like it was a different world. With a different person. 'It was... it was a bad time. For both of us.'

'He took advantage of you?'

She knows Josh is scrabbling around, looking for an explanation as to why Freya and Robin might have kissed. But that isn't it.

'No, he didn't. I kissed him. I think.'

'You think?'

'Listen, Josh. It's not important, please.' She goes to take his hand, but he pulls away. 'Let's forget all of this. Sit on the sofa. Have a nice evening together.'

He shakes his head. 'I can't... Freya, I'm sorry. I need to think.'

And with that he walks away from her, his head down. She watches him go, followed by the bang of the front door and the noise of his car engine outside. She desperately wants to call him back. To make things better somehow. She feels the lump grow in her throat. The tears that have been threatening for so long have nothing to stop them now.

She will lose Josh if she doesn't come clean. And in the process, she has rejected Robin. The thought of losing Robin hits her, almost harder than the thought of losing Josh. How has he become so important to her, over the last year? All that time spent together, through the aftermath of Jon's death. His unwavering presence, unquestioning support.

He asks one thing of her, to keep her mouth shut, and she can't even do that.

She sits quietly in her kitchen, crying softly in the darkness. And wondering, how has this all gone so wrong?

53

Sunday

It's fucking freezing. Robin stamps his feet on the hard mud, blows on his numb fingers. It's a temporary relief from the cold, but not much.

The sky is bleached white by clouds. He's standing next to Liam in the middle of the grounds of a stately home. Patchy grass; a few trees, barely sticks, their branches refusing to show even the slightest hint of spring. A muddy path is in front of them, on which scantily clad women and men run past.

'It would have been warmer to run the damn thing,' Robin grumbles.

'You know as well as I do that you can't manage a half-marathon,' Liam replies and Robin has to admit he's right, muscles protesting from his overenthusiastic sprint yesterday. 'Look, there she is!'

Accompanied by glove-muffled clapping, Liam and Robin shout as loud as they can when Liam's girlfriend, Lizzie, runs past. She's in shorts and a T-shirt, her race number pinned to her chest. She sees them and smiles. A brief wave and she's gone.

'Come on,' Liam grins. 'I'll buy you a coffee.'

They walk briskly towards the finish line. Robin checks his watch. Even at Lizzie's brisk pace, he estimates they have half an hour to kill before they need to cheer again.

They stop at the food van and Liam orders two coffees, then adds a bacon sandwich to the order.

'You want one?'

'Go on then,' Robin agrees, quietly thinking that the bacon sarnie habit will have to come to an end soon. He's not getting any younger, and nor is his metabolism.

They take their order and carry it to a bench on the opposite side, sitting down. Robin can feel the cold wooden slats through his jeans and regrets not wearing an extra pair of socks.

'Imagine willingly being out in weather like this on Christmas Eve,' Liam comments through a mouthful of bacon. 'How's the bloke with frostbite doing?'

'Waiting to see. Still a chance he might lose a few fingers.'

Liam raises his eyebrows. 'And you don't have any idea who did it?'

'We have our suspicions,' Robin says. The Sam/Sara connection bothers him. Two people whose affair directly links to both Alex and Mike. But how to prove it? He wonders what impact their new strategy will have on their suspects, and then debates whether Freya will go ahead as planned.

He sits glumly next to Liam, finishing his sandwich.

'What's got into you today, anyway?' Liam asks. Robin's bad mood is a stark contrast to Liam's enthusiasm for life.

'Nothing. I'm fine.'

'Clearly,' Liam replies.

Robin rolls the napkin in a ball and pushes it into his pocket.

'So it's all going well, then. You and Lizzie?' Robin asks, forcing conversation. 'Must be for you to give up your Sunday morning and drag me out here.'

'Yeah.' Liam beams. 'Really well. She's…' He pauses. 'She's not Georgia, but that's a good thing. I like that she's different.'

Robin nods. He gets what Liam's saying. There's no point trying to replace what you had.

'How did it all go yesterday? With the car?' Liam asks.

'Fine,' Robin replies bluntly.

'And Freya had a good New Year's Eve?'

'I think so, yeah.'

'Right.' He can feel Liam's stare. 'Rob,' he says slowly. 'Has something happened? Between you and Freya?'

'No.' Robin opts for a straight-out lie. The truth is too complicated.

'Because Freya is usually all you talk about. What Freya thinks about the case, what the two of you have been up to. That, and how much you dislike her boyfriend.' He pauses again. 'Is it about him?'

Robin frowns. 'Kind of.'

'Did you tell her how you feel?'

'How I…? No, Liam. It's not like that. Freya and I… We…' He shakes his head. 'It's not like that.' He sighs, noticing Liam's confused face. 'We had an argument, okay? A difference of opinion. We'll sort it out.'

'I hope so. Because your mood, well.' Liam smiles. 'Let's just say it's not great today.'

'Point taken,' Robin replies. He cups his hands round the warm coffee cup then takes a sip. 'That woman on New Year's Eve,' he says, quietly. 'She told me to call her.'

'She did?' Liam looks up, surprised. 'Jo, was that her name? And are you going to?'

Robin smiles weakly. Liam knows him too well. 'I might,' he says.

'You should. It would be good for you.'

Robin sits back on the cold bench, watching the first runners come in. With finish times of just over an hour and a quarter, these athletes were something else. Barely skin and bone, wearing singlets and shorts in these ridiculous temperatures.

He realises with a sting: everyone has someone in their lives they put ahead of Robin. Freya has Josh. Liam has Lizzie. Josie and Finn have each other. Steph has this new bloke; barely met and he gets priority. Who does Robin have?

He thinks about the kiss with Jo. He needs something new. Something with promise, and potential. A break from this. From thinking about Freya.

He feels a tap on his shoulder; Liam is standing up, moving towards the sidelines.

'Come on, grumpy. Lizzie will be here soon. Get ready to cheer.' He sees Robin's miserable expression. 'You'll sort it out. You and Freya,' he adds. 'You've argued before. It was fine then, right?'

Robin stands up slowly. 'Yes, but…' he begins, but Liam is now screaming at the top of his voice as Lizzie sprints past.

But this is different, he thinks.

54

Another night, no sleep. Freya doesn't even try any more.

She sits in the semi-darkness on the sofa, laptop resting on her knees. She logs on to her emails, hoping for a report from the lab, maybe a response from the tipline. Anything to progress the investigation.

But only an email from Coombes and Rosewood waits – a certified copy of Alex's last will and testament, now that the warrant has come through. She clicks it open, curiosity making her sit up straighter.

It's short. Dated the fifteenth of September, two months after his diagnosis. David Coombes appointed as executor – unsurprising. She scrolls down quickly, interested in where the remainder of his estate is going. Alex Reynolds didn't have much. Money invested in his small house, and that was it. But maybe it would provide an indication of where his head was before he died.

And here it is. Split three ways. To Cancer Research; an organisation called LawWorks; and the last third to the Family Holiday Association. She googles two: LawWorks are a charity providing volunteer lawyers to people in need of legal advice, and the Family Holiday Association offer short breaks and day trips to families who otherwise couldn't afford them.

Freya slumps back on the sofa and rubs her eyes. What does that tell her, apart from the fact that Alex Reynolds was a thoroughly decent bloke? There was no illegitimate child on the side. No dying declaration incriminating him or his friends. She's tired of getting nowhere, and pushes her laptop to the side with frustration.

What do they know for sure? Alex died from a lethal combination of hypothermia, alcohol and pre-existing terminal cancer, compounded by a massive overdose of morphine. The same morphine that knocked his friends out, leading to Mike Williams' frostbite. They have a wiped bottle of oramorph, a jumble of prints on bottles and an ancient car in the lab.

A crime scene in a pub, an old argument. A pending divorce, an affair.

A jigsaw of circumstances and exhibits. Nothing that lines up enough to make an arrest.

She flicks the television on, leaves it playing out a crappy film, while she dozes on the sofa. There's no point going to bed. She'll only worry about the case. And Josh, and their argument. About Robin, and the animosity between them.

Light trickles into the room just past seven, waking her from her light sleep on the sofa. She squints at her phone: nothing.

But she remembers she has a job to do, even though it's Sunday. She is still employed; Robin is still her boss.

She gets up and drags herself to the shower.

–

The second cup of coffee goes down fine; the third makes her shake. She sits in a borrowed pool car – her own pastel-blue Fiat 500 is much too conspicuous – down the street from Meg Carlton's house. Waiting.

There's been no sign of Meg all day. What if none of them read the papers? What if they don't contact one another? What if – since they don't have any evidence to support their theory – The Five are actually innocent?

But then the front door opens. Freya scoots down in her seat as Meg Carlton comes out of her house, gets in her car and drives away. Freya starts the engine quickly and follows her. Surveillance has never been her forte, but luckily Meg is a careful driver. She follows speed limits, stops at amber lights and seems to have little interest in the cars around her. Plus, Freya has a good idea where she's going.

A known route. To Sara Williams' house.

55

The loud bang on the door makes Sara jump. A common occurrence – the clatter of an unexpected spoon in the sink, a car's engine racing at night – it sends her cortisol racing. She stands up, hesitant, waiting for her nerves to calm.

The bang again. The hammering of a fist on wood, driven by anger.

'Sara, open up.'

It's Meg. She takes a long breath in, then pulls the latch. Meg storms past her into the house.

'Is he here?' she barks.

'Is who here?'

'Sam. Who else? Mike told me. That you're with him. Again.'

'You've been to see Mike?'

Meg glares. 'Someone has to. When his own wife doesn't care.'

'Fuck off, Meg.' Her eyes are darting to and fro. 'And no,' Sara confirms. 'Sam's not here. So you can leave.'

But Meg stands her ground. 'Is it you?'

'What are you talking about?'

'This. Is this you?'

Meg thrusts her phone towards Sara; Sara takes it then squints at the screen. It shows an article from the local newspaper, an update on the murder investigation into the body. She reads it, dread causing her legs to shake.

> An eyewitness has come forward to help with enquiries. Police state that substantial progress is now being made into the murder of the local man twenty years ago…

'Is it?' Meg repeats. 'Is it you?'

'No! I would never…' She stares at the phone again, willing the words to change. 'Why would any of us go to the police?'

Meg snatches it back. 'I don't know, Sara. You tell me. But it must be one of us. Talking to the police. Nobody saw us. There were no cameras, there was no one around…'

'Maybe there was—'

'No. We were careful.' Meg backs away. 'University was everything to me. The best time.' She stutters, red-faced and rambling. 'And I thought we would always be friends, the five of us. That nothing could break us. But you… you ruined it. This is all your fault. It was then. It is now.'

The words hit Sara like bullets. She feels them physically, searing into her flesh, stopping her breath. The guilt, the shame, the embarrassment – everything she's tried so hard to forget comes flooding back.

'If it hadn't been for you…' Meg continues. 'If you hadn't… If he hadn't…'

Her face is bright red; she's crying now with the power of her rage. Sara envies her – her blatant emotion, her lack of control. For so long she's been numb, blocking it all out by sheer force of will.

'Get out,' she says, hard and quiet. 'Fuck off, Meg. Get out of my house.'

Meg senses Sara's anger behind the thin veneer of calm, and retreats.

'If we all go to prison, it will be your fault,' Meg hisses. And with that she turns, walking quickly out of the house.

Sara takes two paces towards the open door and slams it with all her strength. The noise echoes round the empty house, the windows shake. She feels her hands trembling and walks quickly up to the bathroom, opening the cabinet and pushing two pills – no, four – into her palm, swallowing them down. Then she sinks to the floor. She's crying hard, her body folded in two, her head on her knees, her hands wrapped around them.

She knows. Everything that happened: Meg is right. It was her fault.

56

Freya watches as Meg runs out of Sara Williams' house. She debates what to do – follow Meg or stay put? – but after a few minutes Sara emerges and gets into her own car.

Sara starts the engine and speeds away; Freya follows.

She makes a call, the ringtone sounding over the loudspeaker.

'Pick up, pick up,' she mutters. Robin was supposed to be here, watching Sara Williams, but the street was empty when she arrived. A click, a mumble. 'Robin, where are you? I'm following Sara now.'

'Following Bowen.'

Freya's annoyed. 'We said we weren't going to follow Sam.'

'I changed my mind.'

He's blunt; it annoys her. Whatever the problems between them right now, they have a murder to solve. Plus, she doesn't want Robin finding out about her little conversation in the bar with Sam the other night.

'I'm sure he's headed to the hospital,' Robin says.

Freya notes the roads she's taking. 'Same here.'

'Going to see Mike Williams. The four of them getting together.'

She feels a swell of satisfaction. 'Looks like our little plan worked.'

He grunts. 'Keep in touch,' he says, and hangs up.

A few more twists and turns, but Freya anticipates Sara's moves so it's easier. Sure enough, they reach the hospital and park up; Sara hurries towards the entrance, coat pulled tightly around her as she goes out of sight.

Her phone rings. Robin.

'Sam's met with Sara. Having a bit of a barney by the looks of things.'

'Something in the air,' Freya comments, meaning Sara and Meg, but regrets her words immediately as Robin falls silent. 'Any sign of Meg?'

'No. But Sam and Sara are heading to the ward.'

'Should we follow them?'

'You go. Phone if you need me. I'll get Greg to ping Meg Carlton. See where she's got to.'

Dead space again. Freya feels Robin's rejection hard, an ache in the pit of her stomach. She gets out of the car and walks quickly to the ward where Mike Williams is recovering. But she's distracted, turning a corner and nearly running straight into Sara and Sam.

She jumps back, surprised.

'Well, Detective. We meet again.' Sam's mouth curls slowly into a smile. Freya notices Sara looking sharply to Sam. 'And still without your partner. Have you lost him for good?'

'He's around,' she replies. 'You were here to see Mike?'

'Friendly visit. Cut short by an overzealous nurse. You might have more luck, DC West.'

'I hope so.'

Sara takes Sam's hand, trying to pull him away.

'How is your husband, Mrs Williams?' Freya asks, hoping for a reaction from the woman.

'Ask him yourself,' Sara snaps back. Then she catches herself. 'He'll be home in a few days,' she adds.

'And what will you do then? Given your pending divorce?'

Sara throws daggers with her eyes. 'That's no business of yours.' She pulls at Sam again, but he resists, putting his arm tightly around her.

'I hear you've made progress on your investigation, DC West?' he says. 'It's all over the papers that you'll be able to make an arrest soon for that murder in Portswood.'

'It's a pity the reporter couldn't have been more discreet,' Freya replies, returning his smile. 'But yes. We hope so. And then there's the small matter of Alex's death.'

Sam Bowen stares at her, the smile rigid on his face. 'Good luck with that,' he says. Then he turns and the two of them walk away. Freya watches them go, hand in hand. Over twenty years separate their relationships, Mike Williams in between. She wonders about a history like that. How many shared lies bond them? What could that do, to a person?

If they were involved in the murder of Kevin Gillis twenty years ago, would it be possible to get them to talk? To divide them, make them discard their allegiances. How could they ever get in between that history?

Before she can think any further, Robin appears at her side. He looks as tired as she feels, dark rings under his eyes. He hasn't shaved that morning.

'Mike Williams called,' he says. 'He wants to talk.'

57

Mike Williams sits up straight in his bed. Robin has walked through the hospital in silence, Freya by his side. He wants to ask, *have you? Have you told him?* But something about the look on her face tells him she hasn't.

He knows he has things he needs to say. Apologies to make. He didn't mean to be so rude, but the hurt had taken over. And now? Now he feels things might be unrepairable.

That morning he'd gone against their plan and followed Sam Bowen. Something about the look on Freya's face last Friday morning when he'd mentioned him had made Robin curious. She'd been hiding something. So he'd driven to his block of flats and parked outside, looking up at the impressive historical façade. Robin remembers the fuss when this building was renovated. Planning permission granted to restore a Grade II listed building, but everyone had known copious amounts of money had been involved: both in the building work and the deals made. This was not social housing. This was for the rich and powerful. People like Sam Bowen.

Greg had told him Bowen was here, his mobile phone busy with calls. Robin waited, patiently, until he saw Sam emerge from the building. Groomed, clean-shaven, he headed straight to where Robin was parked.

There was no point in hiding. Robin opened the door and leaned against the side of the car, waiting. In stark contrast to Bowen's expensive-looking sweater and chinos, Robin was wearing an old woolly jumper, jeans and his grubbiest pair of Vans.

'Should I consider this harassment, Detective? Should I call my lawyer?'

'Your lawyer's dead, Mr Bowen.'

Sam laughed. 'I like my legal counsel slick and well paid, and Alex was neither.' He paused, looking at Robin. Robin held his silence. 'I must admit, I preferred your colleague tailing me. She was more fun. You need to up your game, DS Butler.'

'We'll have what we need soon enough, Mr Bowen.'

'I wasn't talking about the case.'

'Excuse me?'

'DC West. And you. That's not something that works. It doesn't take a trained eye like mine to see that. Pretty, intelligent. And...' Bowen tilted his head to one side, appraising him. 'You. Equity theory, DS Butler. We are attracted to those who match us, in physical attractiveness, IQ, age, emotional intelligence. You have that strong, silent thing going on, but a woman like her? She needs more than that.'

'We're not—'

'Sure, sure.' Bowen shrugged, dismissively. 'That's the official line, I get it. Having a relationship with your partner, it's not allowed.' He chuckled and Robin had felt his hands clench. 'Not that it'll be going on for long.'

He turned and walked away.

Robin got back in his car, resolution restored. The arrogance of that man. After a moment, the red R8 had emerged from the underground car park, engine growling. With a crack of exhaust, it tore off, Robin following, the Volvo barely able to keep up with the supercar's acceleration.

But he knew where he was going.

Robin arrived at the hospital with every intention of following. But he stopped. Something held him back from finding Freya. The self-doubt that Sam Bowen had only confirmed: he wasn't good enough. Never had been. Never would be. Not for Freya.

Josh is the better man. And he shouldn't get in the way of her happiness. With his words last night, Robin had put distance between them. Distance they needed in order to get on with their lives.

Then his phone rang. And he had to move.

–

'That was quick.' Mike Williams' face flushes as they approach his bed. 'Did you…'

'Sara and Sam don't know we're here to see you,' Freya says, and instantly Robin sees his relief. Then anger.

'Sara and Sam.' He shakes his head, a look of disgust on his face. 'I feel so stupid.'

'How could you have known?' Freya asks.

'Because it was always them. From the beginning. I was a temporary… distraction,' he finishes bitterly. He looks at Robin. 'And I've had enough. I want to make a statement. You'll need to record this. Make it official.'

Robin takes his phone out of his pocket and clicks it on, placing it on the patient table in front of him. They sit on visitors' chairs at Mike's bedside.

'And I'm assuming my doctor has given you the all-clear to interview me? That I'm in my right mind, clear of drugs?'

Freya nods. 'I spoke to them a moment ago. You'll be going home soon.'

Mike scoffs. 'To what? They haven't made any decisions about my hands. I can't drive. I can't type. I can't even operate my fucking phone.'

'You'll have physio. You'll adapt.'

'Yeah, while she divorces me and moves the kids in with *him*. No. I won't let her get away with it.'

Robin's breath catches. This is it. 'Get away with what?' he asks slowly.

'Drugging us. Killing Alex. Leaving me like… like this.' He holds up his bandaged hands. 'I know she did it.'

'Sara? You saw her?'

'No.'

Robin feels his hope fade. 'So how…'

'You know Sara's a GP?' They both nod. 'Well, since the beginning of December, she's been behaving oddly. Sneaking around, looking guilty. I thought it was just an affair, but then I realised it was more than that.' Mike looks at them both, his face triumphant. 'She's been stockpiling drugs. Writing prescriptions in my name and taking them to a variety of pharmacies in the area.'

'But someone would have noticed,' Freya says. 'The similarity in surname, surely?'

'Williams is common. And she'd go to a different pharmacy each time. I found a label in the bin, I thought it was odd. So I went on the NHS app and, listed under medicines, was all this stuff I've never touched in my life. I didn't even know what they were. Benzodiazepines, antidepressants. She was getting it all under my name.'

'Why do you think she was doing that?' Freya asks.

'I don't know. Perhaps she needed them herself and didn't want it on her record. I looked for them, all over the house, but I couldn't find them.'

Robin feels Freya glance his way. It's prescription fraud, but by no means murder. Especially as these aren't controlled substances.

Mike Williams sees the exchange. He smiles. 'I was going to confront her, but before I did, I checked one last time. Last week. Just before we were due to meet Alex at the beach.'

He pauses. He looks at their faces, waiting eagerly.

'She'd requested a new prescription. She'd collected it that day. For oxycodone,' he says. 'Morphine.'

58

'We need to speak to Baker,' Robin barks as they dash away from Mike Williams. His mobile is already in his hand, buttons being pressed.

Freya wants to talk to Robin, attempt to dispel the bad feeling between them. But now is not the time.

'Guv… yes. Yes, I'm sure. Yeah, we'll come.'

Robin hangs up the phone and faces Freya. 'He wants to discuss it. I'll head over now.'

'I'm coming too.'

'Suit yourself,' he says, and strides away without waiting.

She chases him back to the car park. She gets into the passenger side of his Volvo as she has done a thousand times before, abandoning her own car in favour of a conversation with Robin. She can get it later; this is more important.

'Robin, can we talk?' she tries once they're driving.

'Freya, you made your choice,' he says abruptly. 'You want to tell Smith, and that's fine. But don't expect me to be happy about it.'

'I'm not—'

'No,' he replies, cutting her off. He says it quietly, but his tone, the finality, makes her recoil. She sees him retreat into himself, his face closed off. 'I want to focus on this case. Get it done. Then we can decide where we go from here.'

'Where we go...' Freya's shocked. 'You don't mean request a transfer?'

Robin glances her way, then back to the road. 'You think this is workable?' he says. 'This?'

She retreats into silence. This isn't what she wants. Not at all. She doesn't want to go back to being a typical DC, the dogsbody. The person the DS or DI gives all the crap to. She wants to work with Robin. Their little team, where she's listened to, where she knows instinctively what Robin will do next.

But then she's distracted. After about fifteen minutes Freya looks up in awe, as Robin pulls down a track and stops in front of some large gates. Robin leans out of the window and buzzes; the gates open without a word. The tyres crunch on the gravel as they cruise slowly down the long driveway, pulling up in front of a grand house. The front door is already open, their detective chief inspector waiting in the cold air.

The whole situation seems bizarre. The contrast of Robin's crappy Volvo next to the shiny new Range Rover. Baker, out of his usual smart suit, in tracksuit bottoms and a sweatshirt. He looks every inch the ex-boxer, except for the tweed slippers on his feet.

Robin gets out of the car, and the two men greet each other warmly.

'Happy New Year, guv,' Freya says, feeling awkward.

'Freya, good to see you. Come in, come in. Let's get tea.'

They meet Baker's wife, Tina, a curvy, immaculately groomed lady who hugs Robin tightly. Baker shows them through to the kitchen, where he makes teas and coffees for all. It's certainly a novel experience, being made a drink by her normally intimidating boss. Robin fetches milk from the fridge without being asked.

'It's like you've never left,' Tina remarks, as Robin fetches spoons and the biscuit tin from the cupboard. She turns to Freya. 'Rob came to stay with us for a bit, didn't you?'

'Only a week or so,' Robin says. 'And I'll never be able to repay you for that.'

'And you never need to. Did I show you the new painting we got for the hallway? Come and see.'

She sweeps Robin out of the kitchen. Freya finds herself tongue-tied as Baker hands her a mug of coffee.

'I know Robin's told you. He was in a bad way after Georgia and the boys died. He was out of the Priory, but we didn't want him home alone so he came here.' He squeezes her shoulder warmly. 'I've seen the difference since he's been partnered with you. He's a different man.'

Freya nods, feeling tears threaten. She doesn't trust herself to speak.

'Come through to my study. Robin will be along once Tina's finished chewing his ear off about the kids.'

Baker's study is all dark wood and racing green. A huge bookshelf runs the length of the back wall, a massive desk in front. He gestures to a sofa on the left-hand side and she sits down.

'So, our little plan worked. The local rag came through and published what we asked?' Freya nods. 'Tell me about Mike Williams. Robin said he's dropped his wife in it.'

'Yes. Apparently, she's been taking prescriptions out in his name. Including morphine.'

'And he can prove it?'

'He showed us the app where the prescriptions are recorded. On his phone.'

'No fingerprint recognition to get in, I assume.'

Freya stops, speechless. She assumes Baker's referring to Mike's unfortunate condition, his hands useless and bandaged, but the comment is so out of character for her normally strait-laced boss that she doesn't know how to respond.

'That's so wrong, guv,' Robin says from behind her, coming in and sitting down, his coffee in his hand. 'And no. Facial.'

Freya looks back to Baker; there's a wicked grin on her boss's face.

'Sorry, couldn't resist,' Baker chortles. 'Have you got the original prescriptions yet?'

'No, but we will once the pharmacies open tomorrow.'

That's the proof they'll need. Sara's signature showing she collected the drugs in her husband's name.

'And why was Mike Williams so keen to get his wife arrested?'

'Spite. Jealousy. Anger. All the original sins,' Robin replies. 'There's still a chance he could lose fingers, so I'm guessing that her visit to the hospital with her lover in tow was a step too far for the man.'

Robin's phone starts to ring, and he puts it on the desk in front of them.

'Jess,' he says. 'You're on speaker with DCI Baker.'

'Afternoon, guv,' she says, the Crime Scene Manager's voice loud and clear. 'Working on a Sunday, too?'

'Not out of choice, Jess,' Baker replies. 'Butler doesn't seem to understand the meaning of the word holiday.'

'Or hangover,' Jess replies with a laugh. 'Anyway, your car. The Mini belonging to Sam Bowen back in 2000.

We towed it to the garage yesterday. Ripped it apart this morning.'

'And?' Robin says. Freya sits forward in anticipation.

'We have something. Blood. Not much, because the upholstery and the carpets had been removed. But down the side, it's definitely there.'

Freya smiles. She looks at Robin, and for a second he forgets and grins back. Then the cloud returns.

'Whose?' Robin asks.

'Kevin Gillis. Your murder victim. There's no doubt in my mind that he was in that car at some point. We'll keep looking, there might be something more, but I wanted to let you know as soon as I had confirmation.'

Robin and Freya both look to Baker.

'You've got them,' Baker says. 'Sara Williams for the murder at the beach. Sam Bowen for Kevin Gillis.' He smiles and places his large hands on his desk, leaning forward. 'Arrest them both.'

Part 3

59

There are some arrests that Robin dreads. The unfortunates, the underprivileged. The people who, because of their circumstances, have found themselves in hideous situations where committing a crime seems like the only way out. He has prised screaming children from their mothers, put handcuffed teenagers in the back of his police car. Those are the ones he hates.

But not today.

He stands in Sam Bowen's plush apartment. Next to him, the full-height window shows a view of expensive yachts, sails like porcupine spines, awaiting their plump, primped owners. Sam Bowen glares with cold eyes as Robin recites the familiar words of the arrest. He hears an echo from Freya in the next room.

'Anything you do say may be given in evidence.' Robin stops. Bowen stares. 'Do you understand?'

'You're arresting me for Kevin Gillis's murder,' he says. His voice is calm and impassive. 'Twenty years ago.'

'Yes.'

'I'll be interested to hear what evidence you have linking me to that.' He nods, then holds his hands out. 'Crack on, Detective.'

Robin fastens the cuffs round his wrists. Sam moves towards the door but pauses when he hears the crying in the other room.

'What are you arresting Sara for?' he barks. 'The same ridiculous accusation?'

Sara Williams joins them, her hands behind her, guided by Freya. She's sobbing, unabated tears running down her face.

'Sara,' Sam calls across to her. 'My lawyers will get you out in no time. Sit tight.'

'She says I killed Alex.'

Sam snaps round to face Robin. 'There's no way she killed Alex. This is insane. Hasn't she been through enough?'

'Let's find out, shall we?' Robin replies.

–

They bundle them into separate patrol cars, uniforms ready to take them into custody. Robin knows SOCO have already been dispatched to the Williams' house, Jess in charge. Robin feels that little thrill; they're close now.

With Sam and Sara in custody, they can search their houses, their cars. For anything related to the crimes they've been arrested for. But if they find something else that links them to the other murder, who are they to ignore it? From the beginning Robin has been sure that these five were up to something, and that Sam Bowen and Sara Williams were in the middle of it all.

Greg calls.

'Now we're allowed to,' he begins pointedly, 'I've been going through their mobile data. From about ten this morning there have been multiple calls backwards and forwards between Sara, Sam and Meg. None of them lasting more than a few minutes. But constant. Until about one…'

'When Sara and Sam got to the hospital to see Mike,' Robin finishes.

'Yeah. Get me their handsets. I'll see what else I can find.'

Robin hangs up; Freya comes over. They've already started searching Bowen's flat. She shakes her head.

'Nothing?'

'So far. Except these.'

She holds out a stack of photographs in her gloved hands and flicks through them so he can see. 'They're all of Sara and Sam,' she says. 'Various times in their lives.'

'So this affair has been going on for a while.'

Freya nods. Robin thinks of Sara's kids, wondering who their father is. Has Mike had the same thought? More ammunition to get him to talk.

'Any drugs?'

'Only this.' A new evidence bag, containing a baggie of white powder. 'I'm guessing coke. But not enough for intent to supply.'

'Pity. You head over to the Williams' house. I'll go back to the station.' He sees her about to protest and cuts her off. 'Mina's coming in. And Smith. We're going to need all four of us to interview. Start thinking about tactics for Bowen. Since you know him so well.'

She opens her mouth, then closes it again, her face turning red.

He turns and walks quickly out of Bowen's flat. He's aware he's being a grade-A prick, but he can't help it. He wants her to hate him.

He needs to make the end of their partnership as easy as he can.

60

Freya watches Robin go. Shit. Shit, shit, shit. He knows about her meeting Sam in the bar. And he's not happy.

She has a last chat with the team in charge of the search, then she leaves, heading down to her car and out to Sara Williams' house. Jess waves as she pulls into the driveway. The CSM is outside the front door, talking to a crime scene officer in white overalls. She walks over as Freya gets out of her car.

'Tell me you have something,' Freya pleads.

Jess grins. 'Midazolam, lorazepam, zopiclone. Lots of it. And oxycodone.'

Freya returns Jess's smile. 'All in Michael Williams' name?'

'Absolutely. But what's to say he wasn't involved?'

'Maybe he was. Maybe she'll throw him under the bus, too. Do you mind if I have a look around?'

'Suit up. Be my guest.'

Freya does as she's told, then enters the house. She remembers it from the first time she was here. The tidiness, the order. The knives on a magnetic rack on the kitchen wall, all intact. She opens the cutlery drawer; it's a long shot, but no sign of the knife with the missing tip used to kill Kevin Gillis. Who'd be stupid enough to keep it? Robin's right; it'll be long gone.

A wine rack, half-empty. She opens the door that leads to the garage and switches on the light. A large plastic box for glass recycling waits there, almost full to the brim with empties. She continues her search.

Up the stairs. The wedding photo on the landing that Robin had spotted last week. The boxes of belongings that Mike had started packing. Leaving his wife, even before Alex's death.

Into the main bedroom. Photos of the kids on the wall. She looks more closely. One dark, one blond. She can't see any trace of Sam Bowen in the child's face, but who knows. She frowns. If they'd never stopped loving each other, why had Sara married Mike? Why had they bothered with the charade for all these years? Sara and Sam could have been happy since university, but instead Sara marries Mike, and Sam spends his whole life analysing other people's relationships and screwing up his own. What is the point in wasting time? Being with the wrong person?

She turns her attention to the bookcase in the hallway, running her finger along the line of paperbacks. They all seem like Sara's: pink spines shouting of easy beach reads, followed by a row of self-help books.

A long deafening whine starts up in the hallway: the house alarm. There's swearing, people running, then silence after what seems like hours. Jess pokes her masked face round the door.

'Sorry about that,' she says. 'Some state-of-the-art thing. Goes off at any provocation. Have you found anything?'

'Nothing interesting.'

Jess nods. 'I'm heading off now. Take this oxy back to the lab. We'll see if we can match it to the morphine used to kill your vic on the beach.'

'You can do that?'

'Course. Will call you as soon as I confirm.'

Freya finds herself upstairs alone. The house of a GP. A doctor. Someone that trained for god knows how many years so she could save lives, yet she ends up drugging her husband and oldest friend on the beach. Freya frowns. The evidence is lining up, but something won't sit straight.

But what does she know? After the week she's had, nothing seems right anymore.

61

Sam Bowen's solicitor is wearing a suit that Robin guesses cost more than his bloody V60. The cut is expensive, his shirt crisp, tie glossy silk. Robin recognises him from their voluntary interview with Meg, his abrupt arrival now making sense. Sam must have called the lawyer when he realised what was going on.

Robin shows him into the interview room and leaves them to talk.

He walks back up to the office where Mina is head down with Josh. They look up as Robin joins them.

'Bet he's on double time on a Sunday,' Mina comments.

'At least,' Josh adds. 'Probably getting more in his hourly rate than we do in a day.'

'Well, let's make him earn it then,' Robin replies. 'What have we got?'

He notices Josh is quiet, not his usual annoying self. And when Freya arrives, things are chilly, and not just with her. He feels a glare thrown in his direction, a thoughtful expression that lingers a bit too long.

They talk interview prep, suggest questions for Bowen and Williams, but after a while Robin realises it's only him and Mina talking. Freya gets up and mumbles an excuse about the toilet; Josh says something about coffee.

Mina frowns at Robin when they're alone.

'What's going on with those two?' Robin asks.

'Not just Josh and Freya. There's something distinctly odd with you, Butler, and it's not your usual brand of grump.'

'Freya and I had a disagreement.'

'And is this disagreement related to the lovebirds out there?'

'No. Just me and Freya.'

'Right.' He gets a long stare. But luckily the custody sergeant calls before Mina can question him further.

Freya returns; Josh is not far behind.

'They're waiting,' Robin says to Freya. 'Let's go.'

–

They sit down opposite Bowen and his solicitor. Both look relaxed, sat up straight, a stark contrast to the grunting shitbags they usually face in this room.

Robin issues the standard preamble; the video is started; they all say their names. Robin pauses, his hands resting lightly on the file in front of him.

'Mr Bowen, you lived at 28 Shakespeare Avenue, Portswood, from July 1998 until the end of June 2000, is that correct?'

A quick glance to the lawyer. A nod in return. 'Yes,' he replies.

'And you lived there with Sara Williams, Mike Williams, Meg Carlton and Alex Reynolds?'

'She was Sara Gold then, but yes.'

'Were you close to these four?'

'We were friends.'

'More than friends?'

A pause. 'No comment.'

Robin opens his file and pushes across a photo in an evidence bag. 'This is you with Sara Williams. Would you say this photo shows you being more than friends?'

'Did you never kiss anyone at university, DS Butler?'

'Generally, only women I cared about.'

'So okay, yes. I cared about Sara.'

'Still do?'

He takes a long breath in. 'Yes.'

'Are you and Sara Williams having an affair?'

'No comment.'

Robin decides to shift tack. 'Did you ever go to the Dog and Duck, Mr Bowen? Back in June 2000.'

'That was over twenty years ago. I don't remember.'

'It was the pub Sara worked in.'

'If you say so.'

'Did you meet Kevin Gillis?'

Sam shrugs. 'And he was?'

'The man that owned the bar.'

'I don't remember.'

'Because we have an eyewitness, Mr Bowen. A man who remembers you and Sara arguing in that pub. And you all being kicked out.'

The solicitor sneers. 'An eyewitness identification from twenty years ago, DS Butler? Hardly reliable.'

'He seemed definite to me. Said that you were arguing. That you were splitting up.'

'No comment.'

'Did you own a cream Mini Cooper around that time, Mr Bowen?'

'No comment.'

'DVLA says that you did. And that you sold it in July 2000.'

Another glance to the solicitor. An agreeing nod. 'Yes. I owned a Mini at university.'

'Do you know what this is, Mr Bowen?' Robin pushes a photograph across the table. A dark rusty speck on a cream background. 'It's blood. Kevin Gillis's blood. In your car. Can you explain how it got there?'

Bowen looks at the photo for a long time, his eyes locked on the image. 'No comment,' he says at last.

'We know that Kevin Gillis was murdered on the night of Saturday the seventeenth of June. He was seen for the last time that evening. Until his body was dug up from the concrete of Waitrose car park. Concrete we now know was laid on Monday the nineteenth of June.' Robin waits, watching Sam's face. A few quick blinks, but no other emotion. 'How did his body get there, Mr Bowen?'

'No comment.'

'Did you kill him?'

'No comment.'

'Did you put him in the back of your Mini and drive him round to the car park?'

'No comment.' But Robin notices something: a flash of annoyance.

'Did you bury him in the hole, knowing the concrete would be laid the next working day?'

'How the fuck would I have known that, Detective?'

Robin waits.

'Your theory, your evidence, is pathetic. You have a bit of blood in a car. If this is my car – *if*,' he stresses. 'Then the keys to that car were left by the front door every day. Where any one of my housemates could have picked them up, driven that Mini. Do you want to know where I was that night, Detective? Why that date sticks in my head? Because it was our graduate ball. I was out all night. With

Sara and Mike and Alex and Meg. And hundreds of other people who would confirm if you bothered to track them down.'

'All night?' Robin replies.

'Until about one in the morning.'

'And then what?'

'And then I went to bed. Alone.' He sits back in his seat, resting his arms above his head.

Next to him, his solicitor looks bored. 'You have nothing here, Detectives. A bit of blood in a car is hardly enough for an arrest. I suggest you let my client go.'

'Your client will leave when we say so.'

Freya's been silent throughout the whole exchange, jotting down a few comments on the notepad in front of her. Now, she sits forward in her seat.

'Have you always been in love with Sara?' she asks quietly.

Sam turns his blue eyes in her direction. 'No comment.'

'It's a long time. To be in love with someone who's with another man. That must have been hard.'

'Yes. But her and Mike. That was never love.'

'What was it then?'

'Obligation. Safety. Fear.'

'Fear of you?'

'Fear of the world. Mike was the easy choice. The big, strong copper. The protector. I was a penniless PhD student. What could I offer her?'

'And now look at you.'

But Sam dismisses her comment. 'Love isn't about making sensible choices, Detective. So, yes, if you're looking for honesty. I was in love with Sara Gold, when I was twenty. I'm in love with her now. But did I kill that man? No. There's your honesty.' He glances to his solicitor with a single, decisive nod, then sits back in his seat.

'My client has finished talking,' the lawyer says. 'He will give no further responses to your questions.'

Robin glares at them both. 'Interview suspended at 16.26,' he mutters. Then he walks out of the room.

62

Freya hurries out into the corridor but there's no sign of Robin. She bumps into Mina, waiting.

'Butler said you and I should go ahead,' Mina says. 'Start the interview with Sara Williams.'

'Any idea where he's gone? And have you seen Josh?'

'No, to both. Listen.' Mina puts a hand on Freya's arm. 'What's going on? And don't say nothing, because I'm supposed to be at the cinema with my babies and my husband today, eating popcorn and chocolate buttons, watching the latest mindless Pixar. Instead, I'm dealing with this bullshit.'

Freya takes in her steely gaze, then manoeuvres her into the ladies' toilets.

'Josh thinks there's something going on between me and Robin,' she says, once she's checked there's nobody in the cubicles.

'And is there?'

'No! Well...'

'I knew it!'

'No, Mina. There isn't. But we kissed once. Ages ago.'

'Ha!' Mina's face is jubilant. 'And you told Josh?' she squeaks.

'He guessed. He thinks I'm hiding something from him. But there isn't anything going on between me and Butler.' She sees Mina's dubious expression. 'Honestly.'

'So tell him that.'

'I did. And he...' She sighs and screws her face up. 'I don't know.'

Mina reaches forward and grabs her in a tight hug. 'He'll come round. Stupid man.' She releases Freya, then looks confused. 'So why is Butler pissed at you?'

'That's different.'

'Riiight,' Mina says, puzzled. Her phone starts to ring and she pulls it out of her pocket. 'It's Josh. He's probably wondering where we are.' She gives Freya a sympathetic grimace. 'You'll work it out, hon. Are you coming?'

'I'll be there in a second.'

Mina leaves the loos; Freya waits, leaning against the sinks, composing herself.

She wishes for this case to be over, but the thought makes her stomach drop again. Will Robin request a transfer? She can't bear the idea of not working with him every day, although she knows it'll probably help things with Josh. She remembers her dad's comment at Christmas: the time for a promotion is overdue – is this the push she needs? It doesn't feel like it, not right now.

She walks out into the corridor and heads to the water cooler, taking a cup and placing it under the tap. Her mouth feels dry; she takes a sip, and then another, finding solace in the cold water.

She swallows the last few drops, focusing her mind. It's time for Sara Williams.

–

In the interview room, Sara Williams is sat next to a similarly dressed lawyer to Sam's. Same firm, same bank account, Freya assumes. Mina has started the usual warnings and now announces Freya's arrival to the tape.

Freya sits down. She looks at Sara.

Sara Williams is quiet, her face turned to the table. Her hands are in front of her. Nail polish chipped, cuticles red, nervously picked raw.

'Sara, this can all be over soon,' Freya begins. 'We know you're not the sort of person who would normally get into trouble. You have no criminal record. You're a mother, a local GP. Whatever happened on Christmas Eve with Alex and your husband, please tell us so we can help you.'

She looks up, a slow stare. Her eyes are bloodshot, dark rings like bruises underneath.

'Please tell us what happened that night. You arrived with Mike. At about half eight?'

A flicker of acknowledgement. 'No comment,' she says.

'You used to go to that beach when you were at university. The five of you. Why did you go that night?'

'No comment.'

Freya looks across to Mina, who takes a photograph out of the file and pushes it across.

'These, here, are drugs we've seized from your house. All in your husband's name.' Sara pulls the photo closer, looking at it for a second. 'Drugs we know you obtained illegally through fraudulent prescriptions. And this, here, is oxycodone. You know what that is, don't you, Mrs Williams?'

She stays quiet.

'Morphine,' Freya continues. 'And do you know what Alex was killed with? What drugged you all that night? What meant that your husband got so cold and wet the doctors are still debating removing his fingers? Morphine.'

'This isn't... It's not...' Sara starts. Then she catches the warning look from her solicitor. 'No comment.'

'Did you know your husband has started divorce proceedings against you?'

'No comment.'

'How long have you been having an affair with Sam Bowen?'

'No comment.'

'I was just speaking to Sam. Next door. And he has a lot to say about you.'

Sara meets Freya's eyes. A look of hostility, the first sign of emotion. 'No comment.'

'You speak to us, Sara, and we can help you. If Sam tells us first then I don't know what we'll be able to do.'

She enunciates the words slowly. 'No. Comment.'

Freya pulls the photo back. She thinks of these friends, the bundle of photographs. Their closeness at university then the strange gap of twenty years.

'Can I tell you something, Sara?' Freya says. She leans back in her seat. She's tired. Of all the lies. The secrets. The pretence. 'We found a bundle of photographs at Alex's house. And I've been carrying them around all week. I don't know why, just something about you all was fascinating to me.' Sara's looking at her now, a slight frown on her face. Mina, too; this is not the interview strategy they agreed.

'The closeness. The friendship. The love between the five of you, it's so apparent in those photographs. And I can't help wondering what happened at the end of your time at university that meant you didn't speak for twenty years.'

'We drifted apart.'

'"We drifted apart", yeah, yeah.' Freya waves her hand dismissively. An echo of Sam's frequent gesture, and one she enjoys making. 'That's what you all say. But none of them came to your wedding, and that was barely months after. Why was that, Sara? What happened?'

Sara pushes her lips tightly together.

Freya's sick of this case. Of this lot all lying to her, to each other. But not just that. She's at the end of her tether. The worry about Josh and his feelings towards her. About Robin's hurt, the unknown entity that has been their relationship from the beginning.

'I know something about secrets, Sara,' she continues. 'Not as a copper, but as a person. I know what it's like to hold something so close you feel it physically. Tense muscles, holding your breath so hard you might burst. The worry that one day you'll blurt it out, and the hurt and suffering that would cause to the people you love. The feeling that by staying quiet, you're keeping a part of yourself hidden.' She stops, a quick breath in. 'That because of this secret you don't deserve happiness, or friendship, or even love.' She knows Mina is staring at her now, mouth half-open.

'And I know how that affects you physically. I see you here, now. I can tell you haven't been sleeping. That maybe since whatever it is happened, you haven't had a good night's kip. That you see it in your dreams, their face, and there's nothing you can do to stop it. That you want to tell someone, anyone, but you know that if the people you love knew exactly what had happened to you, what you'd done, there is no way they'd love you anymore. That you're this dirty person, soiled, ruined forever. And I admire you, Sara. For keeping whatever it is quiet for twenty years and still be functioning. Because… because…' She stops now, her words choked in her throat. She wants to say more, but she notices tears in Sara's eyes, spilling over and running down her cheeks.

'No one has a right to know what's going on inside your head. It's up to you if you share. But tell us, Sara, please. We might be able to help you.'

'My client has had enough, DC West,' the solicitor says. 'I don't know where you're going with this so-called interview of yours, but we need an adjournment.'

Freya nods slowly. She's dimly aware of Mina announcing the end of the interview, the video being turned off, and Sara being led out of the room. She feels Mina's hand on her arm, a gentle touch, but she pulls away.

'I'm sorry, Mina. That wasn't professional,' she says, then stands up, darting out of the room.

63

In a room down the corridor, Robin sits watching the video feed. He knew Freya would be good with Sara Williams; the two women interviewing together seemed a good fit, and she's assured, confident. Watching her now, the fact she's still a DC seems wrong. She's not the same cop he met over a year ago; she's experienced, smart. She connects with people. She sees the world positively, in a way he's never been able to.

The door opens. Robin doesn't need to look to know that Josh has joined him; the smell of him is enough to announce his arrival. That shampoo, aftershave, the bloody nice combination that even Robin has to admit is attractive. He sits down next to him, leaning forward towards the screen.

They watch in silence for a moment.

'She's going to "no comment" the whole thing,' Josh says.

Robin grunts a reply.

There's a pause, and Robin feels Josh looking at him. He turns round.

'What?'

'Robin…' Josh begins. Robin frowns. A strange start. Familiar – Robin knows this isn't going to be about the case. 'You and Freya.'

'What about me and Freya?' Robin snaps.

'I'm sorry to ask, and I know how inappropriate this is, but I have to know. Is there something going on between the two of you?'

Christ, this bloke. He pisses Robin off in more ways than he imagined possible. But there's a mixture of insecurity and worry on Josh's face, something he's never seen before.

Robin sighs. 'No. We're colleagues. No more than that.'

Josh nods. He makes a noise, an awkward laugh. 'I'm sorry, I...'

'I'll pretend you never asked.'

'And you won't tell Freya?'

'No.'

Robin turns his attention back to the screen, but something's changed. Freya's manner. She's talking quickly, in the way she does when she's upset. What the hell has happened while bloody Josh has been distracting him?

Freya's talking about secrets, and how she's been feeling, and – oh, shit – what is she going to say? His hand goes over his mouth; Robin debates what to do. Should he go in there, stop her?

But he can see she's getting to Sara Williams. The rigid hostility has gone. She's wrapped her arms around herself, watching Freya closely. Then she starts to cry.

The solicitor speaks, and Sara is taken out of the room. Robin stares at the screen. He wants to reach out to Freya, comfort her. The things she's been through, the conflict she's obviously been wrestling with. Pressure from Josh, pressure from him. None of it has been fair.

She gets up and leaves the interview room; the chair next to him is thrown back and Josh rushes out.

Robin stays, staring at the video. At the space where Freya had been.

64

Out of the interview room, Freya heads straight back to the toilets. She needs space: to think, to digest what she's done. It was unprofessional to go off like that.

She goes into a cubicle and sits on the closed toilet seat. She feels like she's going crazy; all this shit with Robin and Josh, crossing over into the case.

She's not Sara. Her experience has nothing to do with her suspect's. She's been so *stupid*. She pushes her fingers into her eyes. She needs to go home. Have some sleep. Stop drinking.

She hears the main door to the toilets open. Footsteps. Then a soft tap on the door.

'Mina, I'm fine. I'll be out in a sec.'

'It's not Mina.'

She jumps. A man's voice. Josh.

'Freya, I saw you come in here. Are you okay?'

She gets up and slides the lock. The door opens slightly, and she peers out.

'You shouldn't be in here.'

'I know, but… Freya, what you said in there. In the interview.'

'You were listening?'

'Yeah. Me and Butler. Over video.'

Oh, shit, Freya thinks. *Shit*. Robin heard her. Her boss. There's no way he'll want to work with her anymore.

Their partnership, their friendship, it's over. She wants to cry. Go home, hide under her duvet. Never come out.

'And I'm sorry.'

Freya blinks at him. Josh looks miserable. He takes a step towards Freya. 'Everything you said in there. You were right.'

'I was?' Freya's struggling to remember what she babbled in her moment of madness.

'About how no one has a right to know what's going on inside your head. That it's up to you if you share.'

The door opens behind them, and a woman comes in. She stops at the sight of Josh.

'Sorry,' Freya mumbles, then takes Josh's hand and pulls him out of the toilets, down the corridor to the door that leads outside. They burst into the winter air, and stand against the brick wall of the building, hidden in a corner.

'Josh, I...' Freya begins. 'I love you. Only you. Nothing is going on between me and Robin—'

'I know.'

'You do?'

Josh looks embarrassed. 'I asked him. He said you were just colleagues.'

'Oh, right.' *Just colleagues.* Not even friends. But Freya pushes the hurt away, focusing on Josh. 'I want to share every part of my life with you. I do. But some things are complicated.'

'I don't want you to. Not if it hurts you this much. I don't know what happened between you and your ex, but if you don't want to talk about him, then don't. I shouldn't have pushed. It's the past, it doesn't matter.' Freya tries to interrupt him but he's on a roll. He takes both of her hands in his. His shoulders are hunched against the freezing cold. 'What does matter is us. Now. And what we do from here.'

Freya nods.

'Can we focus on that, please? Can I come and live with you? Because I love you, Freya.' He smiles. The old Josh is back. 'And I really don't want to live with my horrible dirty housemates anymore.'

She laughs. 'Yes. Please. Come and live with me. I would like that.'

He leans down and kisses her. 'I've missed you,' he whispers. 'It's been shit.'

'Me too.' She shivers, her teeth starting to chatter. 'Can we go in? Please?' He puts his arm round her and they walk back inside. 'And we need to sort this bloody case out.'

When they get to the incident room, Mina charges up to them.

'Where have you been? Both solicitors are pushing for them to be released. They say we have no solid evidence.'

Freya glances up at the clock. 'We have another twenty hours to go. Where's Butler?'

'No idea. I assumed you'd know.'

'No.' She takes her phone out and dials his number. It rings then goes to voicemail. She cancels the call and looks at the other two. 'It's Sunday night. Nothing is going to happen now. We'll pick this up in the morning. We'll get Jess to confirm the match to the morphine. The pharmacies will find the original prescriptions, so we can make sure that Sara Williams was the one collecting them.'

'And Sam Bowen?' Josh asks.

'That fucker can spend the night in the cells. We know the blood is a match – forward that evidence to his solicitor for him to think about. If he can't present a good explanation for how that got into his car, then we'll call the CPS.' Freya feels a surge of anger. Of determination to get to the end, to the outcome of this bloody case.

'Sam Bowen is involved,' she says, meeting the gaze of Mina and Josh. They look as resolute as she is. 'And I'm damned if he's going to get away with it for any longer.'

65

Robin has to get away from the police station. Space from Freya, and the case, and Clark-bloody-Kent. He needs to think.

There's no doubt in his mind that one – or more – of The Five is responsible for what happened to Kevin Gillis. And that Alex Reynolds hasn't ended up dead by accident. But who, or what is to blame, he just can't fathom.

He heads quickly to the car park, starts to drive home. But something's wrong. A rattle. An awful grating, metal against concrete. He pulls to the side of the road, then walks round to the front of his car.

The bumper is hanging off on one side, dragging against the tarmac. He pokes at the plastic; the damage done by the metal pole on Christmas Day was obviously more extensive than he thought. He swears under his breath, and grabs the roll of duct tape out of the boot.

He lifts up the bumper, trying to return it to its rightful place. But the last mile has torn it to shreds. There's no saving it now.

He gives the bonnet an apologetic pat, then pulls hard. The remainder of the bumper comes away, the car looking pathetic without its protective shell.

He carries it round to the boot and throws it inside. Then he stops. There's a street light overhead, reflecting off the black plastic and highlighting the line of yellow paint where it scraped against the pole. He reaches out a finger. A small fragment comes off and he holds it up to the light. Transfer.

He picks up his phone and dials.

'Jess,' he says when she answers. 'Are you busy? Yes, tonight. Can you come and meet me? And bring a full evidence kit.'

66

Freya finds Robin's absence strange. She tries his phone again. It rings out. She leaves him a message, telling him to call. Please. Where could he have possibly gone? And in the middle of a case.

She remembers Sam Bowen's words at the bar on Thursday night. The psychologist's assertion that there was something between her and Robin, their feelings more than platonic. She thinks about the interview Robin overheard: her own speech about secrets and the lives they destroy.

With a final reassuring kiss to Josh, she says she needs to go home and get some sleep. But instead, she takes a different route. To Robin's house.

The place is dark when she arrives. The curtains are open and she peers through the window into the shadows. She's worried. She goes round the side, through the gate into his garden. She takes the spare key from where she knows he hides it then lets herself through the back door into the kitchen.

She calls out as she steps inside. It's warm, the central heating on. She wonders why she's there. Does she seriously think he would have done something to himself? Maybe, she acknowledges with a fresh burst of concern. She turns a light on.

It's odd being here without Robin. She knows his house almost as well as she knows her own. In the cupboard on the right is a box of decaf teabags he buys for her. There's a sweatshirt thrown over the back of a kitchen chair, his favourite, that she's put on in the past when she's been cold. She places a hand on it now, then picks it up and holds it to her face. It smells of him. A mixture of washing powder, freshly made coffee, lemon shampoo. His skin, late at night when he falls asleep on the sofa and she has to wake him. Warm and soft.

She puts it down quickly. What is she doing? He's clearly not here. Where the hell is he? Gone to Liam's probably, or maybe to the pub. Who knows. But he's not her responsibility. They're *colleagues*, she thinks bitterly. Fucking workmates.

She heads towards the back door to leave, but as she goes, she sees a mug, left dirty in the sink. She looks at it. It's the Mr Brave mug, the one she gave him for Christmas. The present she assumed he hated. It has coffee grounds in the bottom; he's been using it. So he must like it, after all.

Her phone rings, making her jump. She looks at the screen, expecting it to be Robin; a flare of disappointment when it's not.

It's Josh. 'Where are you? You're not here.'

'I'm on my way back now,' she replies. 'Give me fifteen.'

She puts the mug back in the sink, and heads home to her boyfriend.

67

'You take me to the nicest places, Butler,' Jess says. They're standing in the car park behind a Tesco Express, Jess loading the evidence into the back of her van. It's bloody freezing, and Robin's coat is offering no respite from the penetrating wind.

'Thanks for doing this, Jess,' he replies.

'I hope it pays off.'

'When do you think you'll have the results?'

She gives him a disparaging look. 'Tomorrow's Monday. Everyone's back in the office.' He waits. She sighs. 'I'll do my best.'

He thanks her again and they both get in their cars.

He drives back to the police station, deep in thought. This whole time, this whole investigation, something hasn't felt right. Like a piece is missing, something that will make it all come together.

He gets to the office, glad to see it empty, and takes his coat off. He sits cross-legged on the floor next to his desk, ripping pieces of paper into quarters and writing the evidence on the scraps. Sara Williams and the drugs she shouldn't have. The argument in the pub, twenty years ago. The five of them getting together at the beach after all that time apart.

He stops and thinks, the pen paused in his hand. Then he picks up his phone. He scrolls to photos, looking for the ones he took of his Volvo mashed up against the pole on Christmas Day. In the background is Sam Bowen's R8. Next to it, a white Nissan Leaf. Meg Carlton's. A Seat Alhambra next, a family transporter. He pulls up the PNC, types in the plate. Belonging to Sara and Mike Williams. Three cars. All abandoned as their owners were taken to hospital. One missing. The man in the mortuary.

He scowls at the photo. Is it significant? He has no sodding idea.

He goes back to his pieces of paper and what they know. Sara being fired. The blood in Sam's car. The morphine in Alex's thermos. The divorce. The missing knife. The photographs.

Freya is still carrying round the bundle of photos from Alex's drawer, but a few of the ones from round the house have been seized. He gets up and goes to the storage cupboard, opening it and rooting around until he finds what he's looking for. Two, in frames. Not out on display but left in another of Alex's drawers. He turns one of them over, as he remembers the writing in biro on the rear of the shots in the box, then levers up the metal prongs and takes the cover off.

There's nothing on the back of the photo and, disappointed, he goes to replace it. But then he realises there are two: one is hidden behind the main picture on display. Perhaps it had been there first, replaced by a newer, more exciting shot. Perhaps Alex had been hiding it. Either way, Robin pulls it out.

It's the five of them, sat together, squinting into sunlight. All of them look young, and there's a date electronically etched onto the picture, as they were in those days. *04 07 98*, it says. Robin mentally does the calculation: the end of their first year at university.

Sam and Sara sit close together, his arm over her shoulder, her leaning into his chest, smiling happily. But it's another pairing that makes Robin stop.

He picks up his phone. 'Can you do me another favour?' he says when Jess answers.

'Fuck's sake, Butler. Do you know what time it is? You owe me big.' There's a pause. 'Go on then,' she snaps.

'Do you still have the blood samples from all five victims?'

'Yes. Why?'

He pauses. It's no more than a slight suspicion. Probably wrong. And he knows information like this won't be admissible without a warrant. But if it's true? If he's right?

And he explains, Jess growing quiet at the other end of the line.

68

It's worse here. Much, much worse.

The thin veneer of control that Sara has managed to construct has gone and, along with her pills, her calm. She hears the voices of men outside her door. Men who tell her what to do. Men with handcuffs and restraints.

Men in charge.

They ask her if she needs any assistance, if she's on any medication. She shakes her head, no. If they'd asked, 'Are you a risk to yourself?' then they might have been on to something.

She thinks about what she can do to make this stop. The panic, the hateful voices in her brain. Her breathing comes in jerks. Her heart races. She paces the tiny cell, considers banging her head on the wall, knocking herself out. Her only option without sheets or drugs or rope or razor blades.

But her children. Freddy and Tabs. The thing that stops her, that always holds her back. She spoke to her mother earlier; it hadn't gone well. And who could blame her? Her daughter, arrested on suspicion of murder. But at least she agreed to keep the truth from the kids. Sara would get out. She'll be home soon enough.

She hopes.

And then she has a thought. It's radical. It's unexpected. She could tell the truth. She liked the police officers earlier. The two women. There is a shared experience there, a life lived as female. With the barely disguised threats and the innocent catcalls and the men that stand just that bit too close at the bar.

For years she's told herself that she's fine. That's it now, it's done. But denial is there for a reason. Her defences have been inside her for so long, they're built-in. Another skeleton beside the bone, keeping her upright. But now?

You deal with things when you're ready.

And it's time.

69

Monday

The call from the solicitor comes early. Freya races to the station, surprised to find Mina down in custody, the lawyer ready.

'Mrs Williams would like to speak to you. But only to you, ladies.'

Freya throws Mina a puzzled look. She shrugs in return.

'Have you called Butler?' Mina whispers.

'No answer.'

Freya leads the way to the interview room where Sara Williams is already waiting. She looks up. Her eyes are red from crying, her cheeks puffy. Freya and Mina sit down opposite then wait for the solicitor to do the same, but he closes the door as he departs.

Freya looks to Sara, confused.

'I asked my solicitor to leave. I don't need him for this.' Her voice is quiet.

'Should we...' Freya says, gesturing towards the video.

Sara nods. 'Please. I want this recorded. It's been long enough.'

They start the proceedings. Freya waits.

The silence is strange. The room feels charged, an unfathomable energy. Something significant is about to happen. Sara Williams sits up straight, her eyes focused on her hands resting, fingers interlocked, on the table in front of her.

Then she slowly lifts her head.

'Twenty-one years ago,' she says, her voice soft but clear. 'On Friday the ninth of June, 2000. I was raped.'

70

The date is permanently etched on her brain. Ninth of June 2000. She even remembers the time she got there: after closing, about midnight.

She was out with the others. To The Hobbit, a pub down the road. It was a warm night and they sat on picnic benches outside, drinking pints of watered-down Foster's and sickly-sweet bottles of Reef. The five of them, as it always was. The blessed relief of exams completed, but prior to results coming out. Anything was possible. Their whole futures ahead of them.

University was coming to a close. They wouldn't live together anymore. The end of an era. Sara had a room in halls, closer to the hospital. The rest – scattered across the country. But drunken conversations were had, slurring and hugs and reassurance. They would still be friends. Best friends. The Five.

That night, alcohol made her bold. She stood up from the bench, downing the last half of her alcopop.

'I'll meet you at home,' she declared. 'There's something I have to do.'

The others cheered. They knew where she was going. To poor students, money owed was important.

She walked purposefully back up Portswood Road, then stopped outside the Dog and Duck. She banged loudly on the locked front doors. After a while, she heard footsteps, and it was opened.

He looked at her, suspiciously.

'Sara, I told you. You're fired.'

She smiled. She knew blondes were his thing, especially young blondes like her. She aimed to use it to her advantage.

'Can I come in? To talk?'

He sighed. 'Fine. But I won't change my mind. I can't have you and your mates turning the place over like that, no matter how pretty you are.'

He held the door open. She walked through, a grin on her face.

'Do you want a drink?' he asked when she was inside.

'Whatever you're having.' She thought she sounded grown up. Smart.

She took a seat on the bar stool. He passed across a tumbler of brown liquid.

'Whisky,' he said, bringing his own to her side of the bar and sitting next to her.

She chinked her glass against his then downed it in one.

It went straight to her head. She'd already had a lot, been drinking since six. No dinner. She wobbled slightly on the stool.

'I wanted to apologise. For the other night.'

He nodded. 'I appreciate that. But I've filled your job already. You can't have it back.'

'I don't want it back. But you owe me. About a week's wages.'

'I don't think so.'

'You do. Sixteen hours. Fifty-six quid.'

'Nope,' he replied with a smile. He knew he owed her that money.

'Come on, Kev,' she said. She flashed her best flirtatious grin. She tossed her long hair over her shoulders. 'I need that cash.'

'How much?'

'Sorry?'

'How much do you need it?'

She paused. He was leaning closer now, his gaze running down from her face to her breasts. Then lower. She had a sudden chill, a bad feeling. But no. It was her money, and she wasn't leaving without it.

'I have it here. Cash in the register. I could get it now.' But he didn't move. 'I just need something extra from you.'

She glanced towards the till, then to the small kitchen behind the bar. She suddenly realised: there was no one else there.

She shifted in her seat. 'What?'

He turned his face slightly, then pointed to his cheek. 'One kiss.'

'Come on, Kev. Give me the fucking money.'

'One kiss.'

She took a long breath in. He's a leery old uncle, she told herself. One kiss wouldn't hurt. She stood up, then leaned closer, barely touching her lips against his bristly cheek.

Then she felt it. His hand, up her skirt. Fingers on the top of her thigh. She jumped back, slapping it away, but he grabbed her arm, digging in hard with his fingers.

'Get off me,' she shouted, pulling back, but he held tight.

'You want your money,' he said. 'You'll have to earn it.'

'Let me go.'

He pulled her closer, his other hand now on her left arm. She tugged away, but he pushed her against the bar. His eyes were bulging and wide, mouth contorted with anger.

'You flirt with me,' he hissed, his mouth next to her face. 'Every night. With your pretty blonde hair and your bright blue eyes. You pretend, but I know. How much you want it.'

She went to scream, to spit, to shout, anything, but his hand was over her mouth. His hand that smelt of old beer, of whisky. Bar grease ingrained into his skin. She fought again and managed to get away, running quickly towards the door, until a searing pain on her scalp wrenched her backward. Her hair, her long blonde hair, in his fist, pulling her to the ground.

She lost her balance, falling to the floor. She knocked her head on the way down; her vision blurred, dancing colours at the edges.

She lay on her back, blinking. Hard wood, sticky floor, the underside of a table. A heavy weight on top of her – him, one hand on her throat. She felt pressure, she couldn't breathe. Her vision swam. *Please*, she pleaded, but she didn't know if she had said it out loud. Her hands flapped, trying to swipe him away. And as the world went black, she thought – no, knew – she was going to die.

She woke. Confused. Darkness, her eyes closed. She heard the sound of metal, a belt buckle. Her breathing came in bursts as he let go of her throat, then grabbed again, pushing hard, her skull slamming against the floor. He was there. Still there. His heavy body on top of her, her face pushed into his chest.

He was inside her. The horror. The horror of that.

Her throat closed in terror; her insides contracted. She opened her eyes, focusing on the light coming in from the window. A reflection on the ceiling above her: a perfect triangle from the street light outside. She stared at that, trying to block out the pain. The repulsion. The paralysing fear.

'This is your fault,' he said. 'You were asking for it. I'm teaching you a lesson for your own good.'

She remembered those words, years later. The guilt as ingrained as the bruises left by his fingertips on her neck. She'd flirted, she'd laughed. She'd turned up there, alone, in a short skirt and low-cut top. *You were asking for it. This is your fault.*

After seconds, minutes, hours – she didn't know – he stopped and stood up. He pulled up his trousers, refastened his belt. She didn't move. She was no longer there. He watched her, then walked away. She heard the noise of the cash register, his footsteps as he came back towards her. She felt his disdain, his disgust. She didn't look at him – couldn't – curled into a foetal position on the filthy floor.

Paper fluttered to the ground next to her. Footsteps. A door closed. Silence. She waited for a few moments more, then slowly opened her eyes. Her skin burned where he had touched her. Muscles ached. She could taste blood, her lip cut by her own teeth where he had put his hand over her mouth. She sat up. The pain was indescribable, but she weakly pulled herself to her feet. Her knickers lay in a screwed-up ball next to the bar and she put them on, then forced herself to place one foot in front of the other, walking out of the pub.

Outside, the noise of students laughing in the street seemed surreal. She caught the edge of people's expressions as she stumbled, head down, towards home. She raised her hand to her head, felt her matted hair, the sting of the bruise at the back. She was dirty, soiled, disgusting, wrong.

After, she looked in the mirror at the bruises that formed, seeing his fingertips etched, like a map, on her pale skin. On her neck, her arms. The inside of her thighs. The perfectly oval stains marking ownership. Where she had been ruined and destroyed.

A woman approached her, touching her arm, and she recoiled. 'Hey, are you okay?'

Sara nodded her head, yes, yes, yes, and kept walking. 'Can I help you?' the woman called, but Sara wanted to be home.

She put her key in the lock, pushed into the house. She closed the door behind her. She could hear music from Meg's room, the one closest to the front door. Meg shouted over the din.

'Sara, did you get your money?'

And she thought of the cash. What she had done to earn it. The three twenty-pound notes. Screwed up on the floor of the Dog and Duck.

71

The room is still. Silent. People walk past on the corridor outside and their footsteps seem intrusive, wrong, in the void left once Sara Williams has finished talking.

'I'm—' Freya swallows, tries again. 'I'm sorry, Sara,' she says.

Sara nods, mute. Freya glances across to Mina who is sitting, stunned, the notepad resting blank on the table. Mina's been crying, the tracks visible on her cheeks, and Freya raises her hand to her face, wiping away her own tears.

Freya clears her throat. Sits up straight. She remembers who she is, that she has a job to do. But also, that she is human. Female. And that this woman has gone through an extraordinary amount of trauma.

'Did you report it to the police?' she asks softly.

'No, no, I couldn't. Who would believe me?'

'We believe you,' Freya replies. Sara meets her eyes, the relief palpable.

'I'd been drinking,' Sara says. 'I knew him. It would have been his word against mine.'

'But the bruises, the evidence—'

'Rough sex. Stupid young girl. Short skirt.' She laughs harshly. 'I know how these things play out, how women are destroyed in court. If it even made it there in the first place. Rape kits left untested in labs, the CPS seizing your phone. We live in a world where misogyny is the norm. And that's now. What chance did I have twenty years ago?' Her voice trails off. Her gaze drops to the table again. 'When I was at school, a woman in my town was raped. A stranger grabbed her one night, there was nothing she could do. She went to the police. She did what she was supposed to, and the man was caught. But I heard what they all said.'

'Who, Sara?'

'The people we knew. My parents. My friends. "She was lucky because she was raped". "He could have killed her". "She shouldn't have been out that late". "No nice man will want her now". Damaged goods.' Sara looks up. She meets Freya's gaze and Freya sees the determination, the hate in her eyes. 'Even the ones that didn't say such awful things… I could see it. The pity. To them, this woman was a victim. I didn't want to be defined in that way.'

'Did you tell the others? Your housemates?'

Sara shakes her head. 'I couldn't. I couldn't say it out loud. What he'd done. All I could think about was how I'd provoked it. What I should have done to stop him.'

'It wasn't your fault,' Freya says. Sara doesn't reply. 'It wasn't your fault, Sara.'

Sara blinks for a moment. Tears fall onto the tabletop. Then she continues without acknowledging Freya.

'I just said he had attacked me. Grabbed me… down there. Then pushed me out of the bar. I told Meg first, and she said… she said…' She takes a long breath. 'She said what did I expect? Going there alone. That she would never have let that happen to her.'

Freya recoils with surprise at the callousness of the response.

Sara continues: 'Then the boys came home and Meg told them. Sam wanted to go back, the three of them, to confront him, but I wouldn't let them.'

Freya glances to Mina. Motive. Sara sees their expressions.

'No. No, they didn't kill him.'

'How do you know, Sara?' Freya asks softly.

'If anyone had motive, it was me. All I wanted to do, after I'd slept, after I'd downed enough alcohol to block out the pain, was to go back there and kill him. The rage, the hatred. I'd never known anything like it.'

'But you didn't?'

'No.'

'And neither did the boys?' Freya challenges. 'You're sure?'

'Yes.'

'This was on the ninth of June, Sara. Just over a week later, Kevin Gillis was killed. Your friends have motive, opportunity.' Freya pauses. 'We found blood in Sam's car, Sara. In his old Mini.'

Sara's head snaps up. 'No,' she repeats, definite. 'He promised me. It wasn't Sam.'

Freya nods. Her mouth is dry. She takes a sip from the plastic cup of water in front of her.

'Do you have those photos?' Sara asks. 'The ones that belonged to Alex?'

Freya nods and picks up the bag by her feet. She takes the photos out, in their evidence bag, and hands them to Sara.

'Can I look at them?' she asks.

'Sure.' Freya doesn't think a little contamination from Sara is going to make any difference. What might help is the emotion conjured up from the memories. At seeing her friends' faces, from all those years ago.

Sara takes them out and holds them tenderly in her hands. The one on the top is a shot of Sara and Alex, drunk, in a pub. Broad grins, pint glasses clinking together.

'We had the same birthday, Alex and I,' Sara says softly. 'Three years, celebrating together, every November. I loved it. No matter how drunk I got, Alex could be relied upon to be worse. So, the embarrassing stories, they were always about him. He said he was taking one for the team.' She sighs in a series of jerky breaths. 'Why would I kill him, DC West? I loved him.'

'What were the drugs for, Sara?'

Sara looks down at her hands. She starts picking at her fingers, a line of skin pulled from the cuticle. An action that makes Freya nauseous, as blood blooms from the edge of her nail.

'They were for me,' she says softly. She lifts her head; she's crying again. 'I thought… I thought if I could get enough then I would take them all. Fall asleep and never wake up. But I couldn't…'

Freya stays quiet, waiting for Sara to talk.

'I always told myself I had that as a way out. If things got too much, if I couldn't take it anymore. Do something. Slit my wrists or… anything. I could do it the right way. I am a doctor, after all.' Her shoulders rise and fall with the force of her weeping. 'It was a consolation, of sorts, but I never felt I wanted to go that far. Then I saw that a body had been discovered. In Portswood. And I knew it was him. That it was Kevin. And it all came flooding back. Like it was yesterday. I couldn't bear it. The smell, the feeling of him… doing that…' She lowers her gaze and sobs quietly into her hands, her head almost resting against the table.

Freya wants to comfort her, to reach across and touch her arm, but given what Sara's told them, she suspects any contact will be unwelcome.

'I'm glad you didn't,' Freya says, instead. 'But what stopped you?'

Sara lifts her head and regards Freya with bloodshot eyes. 'Do you have kids, DC West?' Freya shakes her head. Next to her, Mina replies, 'I do. Two.'

Sara turns to Mina. 'Then you know. The thought of leaving them, it was too much. To do that to them, to shatter their lives in that way. It would be almost as bad as what he did to me.' She smiles now, weakly. 'Plus, I have Sam. We're going to be together now, properly. That future, a promise of a new start with him. I don't know. It helps.'

Freya glances across at Mina, who nods in unspoken agreement.

'Sara,' Freya says. 'We're going to end this interview now. Unless you have anything else you'd like to share?' Sara shakes her head. 'We're going to take you to our family room. It's nicer there. I'll call a specially trained officer who will sit with you.'

'I'm not going back to the cell?' Sara asks.

'No. I need to have some conversations with my colleagues, and then I'll be back to talk to you. Okay?' She waits, but Sara's still crying. 'Thank you for being so brave today.'

Freya gets up; Mina follows, escorting Sara Williams out to the other room down the corridor. Freya walks through to the custody desk and makes a call to the Sexual

Offences Investigation Team, explaining the situation and requesting an STO.

She turns and Josh is next to her, his face pale.

'Fuck,' he says.

'You heard that?'

'I was watching on the video. That poor woman. All this time.'

Freya nods. 'Is Robin with you?'

'No. I assumed you knew where he was. He hasn't been in this morning.' Freya frowns. 'I believe her,' Josh adds, and Freya glares at him. As if that was in doubt. 'I mean, about the drugs,' he says, quickly. 'I don't think she killed Alex Reynolds.'

'No, I don't think so either. I'll call Jess, confirm the comparison results, but then we'll get her released.'

'Agreed. It's more evidence against Sam Bowen, though, right? That he went back later and stabbed him?'

'Exactly.' She frowns. Something feels wrong. The eyewitness in the bar had said that Sara and Sam had split up at the time. 'But for assault?' Freya continues. 'If he didn't know about the rape and that's what he believed happened, it seems a lot to stab the guy?' She pulls her phone out and dials Robin's number. It rings out and she leaves a sharp message, telling him to call her. 'Where is Robin?' she snaps. 'It's his bloody case, and he's gone AWOL.'

'We can interview Sam Bowen again without him,' Josh counters. 'We know what we're doing.'

'We're going to fucking have to.'

-

They walk back up to the office. Freya notices paper scattered round Robin's desk, scraps with his illegible scrawl, screwed up and thrown in his bin. She picks one out, frowning. What was going through his mind last night? She wishes he would just tell her what's going on. She doesn't like this distance, but it's her fault. Robin going off like this, alone. It reminds her of their first case, Robin doing stupid things. That time he ended up beaten and bruised, punched by the bouncer at a club. This time, who knows? It nags at the back of her mind.

Mina joins her and Josh; the three of them stand together, waiting. For the senior officer, the one who isn't there, to give permission to act. Freya rolls Robin's note into a ball and drops it back in the bin.

'Mina, call the CPS,' she says. 'Send them everything we have on Sam Bowen. I want authorisation to charge.' She looks to Josh. 'Let's go.'

72

Sara thought she would feel different somehow, now that the truth is out. But she doesn't. She's still afraid.

She hears the babble of the police station, voices in the corridor, the slamming of doors, shouts from disgruntled parties. She sips her sweet tea slowly. She wants to go home, but what is waiting for her there? The locks on the windows, the alarm, the outside lights that spring on when a fox walks across their lawn. The useless attempts to feel safe when the danger comes from within.

That night, after she spoke to the boys, to Meg, she saw their shocked expressions morph from surprise to sympathy to anger. Once she persuaded them to let it be, leave it alone – I'm fine, I'm fine, I'm fine – she went upstairs to the bathroom. She turned the shower on to full heat and stepped inside. The water scalded her skin, steam rising. She scrubbed until her body was raw. Eliminating him. His fingers. His smell. His DNA, coating her like paint, suffocating every pore.

I'm fine, I'm fine, I'm fine, she thought, taking a pair of scissors and holding them next to her face. Handfuls of wet blonde hair in her hand, she hacked away, leaving piles discarded on the floor.

I'm fine, I'm fine, she repeated as she dried herself with her fluffy towel, the white turning pink with blood. I'm fine.

But the mantra made no difference.

The world was pulled into two. Before and after. Safe and not safe. Years passed; it was always there. A splinter under her skin. Niggling.

In GP consultations, she'd move her chair away to the other side of the room when a man had a sharp nose or the same coloured hair.

The slightest sense of that smell – old beer, sticky floors, ingrained cigarette smoke – and she would be back there. She could just about manage slick shiny wine bars, especially with a few strong cocktails down her throat. But real ale, an unexpected touch, a casual remark. It would stop her breathing, leaving her dizzy and cowed in an instant.

A scarf, anything round her neck. A strange look from a man, and she'd think *he knows, he can tell*. Something was wrong with her. Something is still very wrong.

From watching that woman, all those years ago, she'd learned that few people can cope with a crisis like rape. It's too much. They become tongue-tied, the braver ones resorting to bland platitudes. But Mike Mike had been the constant by her side. Sam had been unable to deal, baffled by her silence. At first, he hadn't known what to say, then all he'd managed was the wrong thing. But Mike had been practical. Solid. Stable. Everything she'd needed. A quick wedding followed, Mike professing his love. She had felt gratitude, in his debt for putting up with the woman she had become. This husk of a human he married.

But duty can only take you so far.

With Sam, she was the girl he once knew. Carefree. In love. It had always been Sam. Before, after. Now.

A woman in uniform arrives in the room. She sits down next to her, gives her another tea. She starts talking, Sara barely listening.

That's enough now, she resolves. She's lived in a different world to everyone else for too long. It was one moment. And the man is dead. Nothing more than bones.

She'll get her divorce. Maybe she'll even find a therapist, get some professional help.

But, despite everything she's telling herself, Sara knows nothing will change.

Because, despite everything, she's still lying.

73

Sam Bowen looks decidedly less immaculate this morning; a night in the cells hasn't served him well. Shirt crumpled, hair in disarray. The standard-issue blue blanket is thrown round his shoulders.

He stares grumpily at Freya as she enters the interview room, his solicitor at his side.

'I have nothing more to say,' he states before they've even sat down.

'Morning, Mr Bowen. This is DC Josh Smith.'

Josh nods across the table; Sam looks at him with interest.

'Where is DS Butler this morning?'

'Otherwise occupied.' Freya places her notepad neatly in front of her. 'We don't mind if you keep quiet, but we do want to fill you in on where we are in our investigation. In case you have anything to add before we charge you.'

The solicitor looks at her with contempt. 'Even if the CPS do agree to the charges, you don't have enough to make them stick.'

Freya smiles tightly. 'Let's see, shall we.' She turns her attention to Sam. 'We've just been talking to Sara. She asked to see us. She told us all about the events twenty years ago.'

She pauses.

'No comment,' Sam says pointedly. But Freya notices a flicker of interest.

'She told us about Kevin Gillis. How he attacked her.'

His forehead creases. Freya sees worry in his eyes. Despite all his arrogance and bluster, she believes that Sam is genuine in his love and concern for Sara. 'How is she?' he asks.

'She's speaking to our trained officers now.'

'She didn't kill Alex.'

'Who did, Sam?'

He stops. His eyes drop to the table. The first sign of doubt she's seen. 'It wasn't Sara,' he says quietly. 'She would never do something like that. She's not that sort of person.'

'But you are, Mr Bowen, aren't you?'

'I didn't kill Alex. And I didn't kill that bloke.'

'So how did that blood get in your car?'

'No comment.'

'Who buried him?'

'No comment.'

'Who killed him?'

'I don't know,' he snaps. His eyes flare. He's annoyed, exacerbated by his worry for Sara. 'But let's talk about your hypothesis, shall we?' he continues. 'The reason why I'm here. You think I killed him.'

'His blood is in your car.'

'So what? He could have been alive.'

'Was he?'

He ignores her question. 'And that's not the only flaw in your logic. Why are the others covering for me? Mike hates my guts – I'm sleeping with his wife. And Meg and I, we've never been close. Alex was the glue that held us all together, and he's gone. Why haven't they turned me in?' He looks at Freya, levelling her with his stare.

'I have to give you more credit than I expected,' he continues. 'Putting that article in the paper. Trying to make us think one of us had come forward. Bravo.' He raises his hands in two slow claps. 'But why hasn't it worked?'

'Perhaps you were all involved,' Freya retaliates.

He points a finger in her direction. 'Okay. I'll play. So, someone killed Kevin Gillis. And let's say he deserved it. How will you prove who, without a murder weapon? Today's law doesn't allow for psychological concepts like groupthink or mob mentality. A jury wants evidence and science, and things they can see and understand.'

'Like blood in a car,' she snaps back.

Freya is tired of all this game playing. She glances to Josh; he looks just as pissed off.

Sam's shaking his head. 'You're wrong about so many things, DC West. You're wrong when you think I killed Kevin Gillis. Yes, I was angry when I found out what he'd done to Sara. She was shaken, yes. She was covered in bruises. But he only pushed her around a bit. It wasn't enough to go to the police, and it certainly wasn't enough motive to kill him.' Freya sees his solicitor tense, a hand on the arm to try and get his attention. 'You talk about this argument that Sara and I had at the pub. Splitting up? That's bollocks. We were together when all that shit went down. We only split up after. When she... when she got together with Mike.'

'Did you drug Mike and Alex at the beach?' Josh this time, interrupting his flow.

'No. For Christ's sake, I don't know who did that. I ended up unconscious, too. Why would I drug myself?

Tell me that.' He stops, eyeing up Josh. A quick appraisal, but Freya's experienced first-hand how astute Sam Bowen can be. 'You're not from around here, are you? Newcastle, right?' Josh stays quiet. 'And the accent is strong, so I'm guessing you've not lived here for long. Moved down recently, did you? Why was that?' He stops, thinking. 'A long way to come for a transfer. And not a promotion, judging from your rank. So, what? Love?'

Even Freya notices the flicker on Josh's face, confirming Sam's assumptions.

'Interesting. Oh! Now I get it.' He looks between the two of them. 'Now it all makes sense.'

'We're not here to talk about me, Mr Bowen,' Josh growls.

Sam sits back in his seat, smug. 'I bet DS Butler isn't a fan. The two of you don't get on, do you? A man like him, rough around the edges, faced with a handsome prick like you.'

'How did that blood get in your car, Mr Bowen?'

'How long have you two been together? Not long?'

'How did you kill him?'

'Less than a year?'

'You're in no position to give me relationship advice. A marriage therapist with two divorces under his belt.'

'I know. The irony.' Sam crosses his arms over his chest. He grins as he turns to Freya. 'Although maybe that should teach you something, DC West. About the consequences of being with the wrong person. When the right one is there all along.'

Josh's eyes flare. 'We're done here,' he barks.

He storms out of the interview room, the door slamming behind him. Freya picks up her notepad.

'Interview concluded at 10.32,' she says and switches off the video.

74

Robin wakes, shivering. Despite his gloves and his hands being shoved deep into his coat, his fingers are numb. He can't feel his toes.

He shifts position against the steering wheel. He debates turning the engine on and warming the car up but decides against it. He leans forward and wipes his hand against the windscreen, rubbing away the condensation. The outside is frosted grey and opaque. He swears. Even if someone did arrive, he wouldn't be able to see them.

He picks up his phone and notes the four missed calls from Freya. He listens to her voicemails, her tone vacillating between confusion, desperation and anger. He sighs. He knows he needs to speak to her soon, and wonders how she's getting on with the interviews back at the station. He knows this is wrong, going off on this quest alone, but he doesn't even know if it will pan out.

And he feels stupid. It's become impossible for him to deny his attraction towards Freya. The growing affection he's suppressed for so long, feelings of more than just friendship. He's not sure he even wants to act on it, but the almost certain knowledge that she doesn't feel the same way – and won't ever, as Sam Bowen has pointed out – is humiliating.

So he hides here. In his car. Waiting. For someone who's not going to show up. In the slight hope that he's right, and they do.

75

Freya's furious. No reply from Robin, and now Josh has stalked off in a temper. Mina is waiting for a response from the CPS; Jess Derby hasn't returned her call.

Where the fuck is Robin?

She sits down at his desk, looking at the random scattering of Post-it notes and scraps of handwriting. She picks up a paper clip, turning it over in her hand as he often does. She mimics him, tapping her middle finger a few times on the desk. Where are you? And what is going through your head, you stupid man?

She starts working her way through the many pieces of paper, then opens his top desk drawer and stirs the mess with a finger. The man is such a slob. Why can't he be tidier? She scowls, getting angrier with each passing thought. Why can't he take better care of himself, so she doesn't have to worry? Why can't he pick up the bloody phone?

She opens the bottom drawer, then stops, surprised at what she sees. It's a small blue gift bag, so out of place among Robin's other possessions. She picks it up and looks at the label.

To Freya. Happy Christmas. x

Written in his inimitable scrawl. But he hadn't bought her anything. He said…

She glances around, then slowly pulls the tissue paper out of the bag. At the bottom there's a small pale blue box and she takes it out, placing it gently on the table. She knows she shouldn't look, but the curiosity is too strong.

She takes the lid off carefully, then removes the tiny fold of padding. She gasps. Underneath is a perfect silver bumblebee on a delicate chain. The workmanship is incredible: tiny lines etched on its wings, fat body with little antennae poking out the top. But it's not just the beauty of the thing; it's the fact he saw it and thought of her. He knew she would love it. And she so does. She wants to take it out of the box and put it on now.

But she replaces the lid, and reluctantly puts everything back as she found it. He hasn't given it to her for a reason, and she wonders why. What had she done wrong?

She puts it back in the drawer and shuts it, jumping as she hears a voice behind her.

'Butler around? I emailed him but he didn't respond.'

It's Jess, holding a few sheets of paper.

'No, he's out. Somewhere.' Freya sighs. 'Can I help? Do you have the results on the morphine?'

'Ah, yes.' Jess takes a seat next to her, shuffles her stack and hands her a page. 'It's a no, I'm afraid.'

Freya sighs with relief. 'Thank fuck for that.'

'You're pleased?' Jess looks confused. 'I thought Sara Williams was your best bet?'

'She was, but…' Freya doesn't want to go into details. 'Let's just say I'm glad we can let her go. But now we have nothing on the Reynolds murder.'

'Ah! Except this. Butler was right.'

'About what?'

'He didn't tell you about our little expedition last night?'

'No...'

'Or the little off-the-books test he made me do?'

'No.' Freya holds her hands out for the reports. Jess passes them over.

'Well, his suspicion was on the nail. You can't use it, but the fibres, the chippings. That's admissible evidence.'

Freya's confused. She starts reading. Blood test results. Human chorionic gonadotropin. Tapings from Reynolds' clothes. Fibres. Paint.

And her mouth opens in surprise.

76

Robin can't sit here any longer. His numb toes are painful now; he needs to get out, walk around. Get some blood moving in his veins.

He opens the car door, instantly receiving a rush of cold salty wind to the face. It stings his nose, sears his lungs; he pulls his scarf up as high as it will go. He hears the ping from his email and opens his phone, seeking shelter against the car and taking a glove off for the fraction of a second he needs to operate the touchscreen. He reads the email from Jess, feeling a triumphant surge. He was right. She was there.

He replaces his phone in his pocket and starts walking from the car park to the beach. The weather has worsened since he was here ten days ago. The wind has picked up, freezing gusts whipping across the pebbles, inciting the waves into white frenzied peaks. He wraps his arms around himself, numb feet losing their grip on the stones.

He stops next to a wooden groyne, topped by the upside-down metal lampshade of a lateral buoy. Rust pushes through the red paint, reminding Robin of a wound, skin ripped, blood bubbling. Scabs and clots and dark brown crusts of tissue. Kevin Gillis, bleeding out on his dirty lino floor.

The crime scene tape has gone from the beach, cones removed. There is no sign that someone died here on

Christmas Day. He walks along to the patch of stones that was Alex Reynolds' final resting place, then looks behind him to the beach huts. Light green, yellow, turquoise. Then one different from the rest: a dark navy blue. He walks up towards it.

It's old, in desperate need of repair. The wood is rough and peeling, and he reaches out, taking a fragment of paint on the fingertip of his glove. Paint found on the clothes they recovered last night. From a charity bin behind the Tesco Express. The door is splintered and cracking; a small rusty padlock holds it shut. He rattles it, half-heartedly. He can't break in; anything he finds as a result will be inadmissible. But he could get a warrant now, with the evidence they've found.

He shelters in the overhang of the beach hut, face turned towards the wood, and takes his phone out of his pocket to call Freya. But before he dials, he hears quick footsteps on pebbles, getting closer. Faster.

And then his head explodes with pain.

77

The man falls. Like the press of a switch, a rapid loss of power, his legs collapse under him. She stares at his prostrate body, crumpled in the wooden porchway of the beach hut. The wooden log drops from her hand.

What has she done? Oh, shit. What has she done?

It's the detective, the nice one. The man from the investigation. She's assaulted a police officer. Maybe killed him. She takes a step towards the body, then reaches out a shaking finger and pokes him. He doesn't move.

It's starting to rain now. She remembers the freezing temperatures, the hypothermia from before, and knows she needs to find shelter. If he is alive, she doesn't want him to freeze to death.

She takes the keys out of her pocket, fumbles with them and drops them on the shingle. She picks them up again, this time managing to open the padlock and pull the door open. The wind grabs and tugs and slams it against the opposite side with a bang. She jumps, glancing around. But the beach is deserted. There is nobody here.

Is he alone? Why would he do that? Why would a detective come by himself? She needs to move him, get him out of sight. Before someone sees.

She grabs an arm and pulls. She swears. This bloke is heavy, unwieldy. She tries a different tactic, grabbing him under his arms and slowly tugging him into the beach hut.

The wound on the back of his head is bleeding profusely. It soaks the front of her coat, her hands, everywhere. It forms a slowly growing puddle on the wooden floor of the hut where he lies.

How is he not dead? He must be dead. All this blood. She could dispose of the body. It was okay last time, until someone dug him up.

What about the sea? He could be swept away. The fishes and the tide would do their work, and he'd never be seen again.

What is he doing here? How much does he know? Will the police turn up soon, arrest her, chuck her in jail? Questions, panic, swirl in her head. She could run. Get on a plane before they know she's missing. She's heard of people doing that, getting away with murder.

But then: a groan. A shifting of limbs. She stares, frozen with fear.

The man moves.

He's alive.

He's awake.

78

Everything hurts. Robin lifts his head; it sings with pain His body is cold. His vision blurry, ears ringing. He's aware of wooden boards under him.

He's lying on his side. He keeps his eyes closed, summoning his remaining strength to move. He can hear someone close by: a pacing to and fro. Two steps one way, two steps back. Quick and frantic.

He opens his eyes and groans quietly. He blinks. The light is dim. He can see boots, jeans.

He looks up.

'Meg,' he says.

She stops. She looks at him with frightened eyes.

'I didn't know you were police. I didn't recognise you. I thought… I thought…' She starts pacing again.

Robin reaches up to his head, then recoils as a bolt of pain races through his skull. When he opens his eyes, his hand is covered in blood. His head feels muddled; he can't think straight.

'Meg,' he says slowly. 'I think you need to call an ambulance.'

'I can't… I can't… I assaulted a police officer. I'll go to prison.'

'You'll be in worse trouble if I die.' Robin feels outside his own body. A pervading sense of calm, despite the sinking realisation that something is horribly wrong with his head.

'Why were you here?' she says. 'What were you doing here?'

Robin winces and pulls himself up to a sitting position. He realises where he is now. There are a few small cupboards in front of him, a gas stove on top. Sand and pebbles on the wooden floor.

'Call 999. Please, Meg.'

'Tell me why you're here!' she shouts. Her voice is strained, her panic more apparent.

Robin closes his eyes. The light makes the headache worse. 'The paint fragments on your clothes, the scarf you tried to donate,' he says quietly. 'We found them. In the Cancer Research charity bin. The one closest to your house. And I know that once we compare them to this beach hut, they'll be a match. And the tapings from Alex's clothes.' He stops. He's finding it hard to talk, every word an effort.

'What do you mean, tapings?' she asks.

'Our lab techs. They took evidence from Alex's clothes, with tape. They capture all sorts of things from the material: tiny fibres, transfer from the things he was near. And they found your scarf.' He points up to Meg's bare neck. 'DNA proves it was yours. Pink fibres from that were found on his jumper, underneath his coat.' He stops again. Closes his eyes for a second, gathers his energy. 'It shows you were near Alex before you went out. You were in his house. You drove him to the beach that night, didn't you?'

She starts to cry, sitting on one of the old wooden chairs opposite.

'Why did you drug them, Meg?'

She lifts her head, tears streaming down her cheeks. 'He wanted us to go to the police. To tell them what happened. But I couldn't have that. Things were finally coming together. For me. I was going to have him. What I've always wanted.'

'Mike.'

'Yes,' she replies. 'She took him from me. And she was sleeping with Sam the whole time. She never loved Mike, it was always about Sam. And when he found out she was cheating on him, Mike came back to me. We were going to be together again. Like we were at university.'

'It was you and Mike at the pub,' Robin says. 'The break-up. That was you.' The two people that looked the same, with similar-sounding names. They'd assumed it had been Sara and Sam splitting up, but they were wrong. It had been Meg and Mike.

'He dumped me, for her. She was still with Sam, but even the chance of being with Sara, that was enough. And then all *that* happened. To Sara. The assault.'

Robin's confused. Assault? Sara? His brain feels muddled; he's weary, desperate to sleep.

'And Mike was there for her. He couldn't let her down, could he? Not after that. And then they got *married*.' Her voice rises to a squeak. 'We couldn't go to the police. Not after all this time. Alex was dying anyway. What difference would it have made? I didn't think I'd hurt Mike. But once the morphine was in the hot chocolate, I couldn't stop Alex passing it round. I only took a sip. Because… because…'

'You're pregnant.'

She stares at him. 'Yes. How do you know?'

'Your fingerprints on the hip flask. I thought it was odd, a hip flask without any alcohol. But you brought it to pretend you were drinking. Same as when they all passed out.'

She nods. 'What else could I do? I had to make out I was also a victim. Otherwise the police would have known. You would have known it was me.'

His vision blurs again; he blinks. 'But...' he mumbles. 'You must have been freezing.'

Meg's still talking, but Robin can't hear now, everything seems muffled. He's vaguely aware of feeling sick, then he turns, vomiting on the floor next to him.

He wipes his mouth with the back of his hand, saliva leaving a trail across his sleeve.

'What happened to...' His voice is slurred, the words not coming out properly. 'What happened to Kevin Gillis?' he says, trying again.

But she's gone. His battle to stay awake is over. The light fades, and everything goes black once more.

79

The blue lights of the police car flash, dancing off paintwork and pavements as they pass. Freya sits mute in the passenger seat as the officer negotiates the narrow roads at speed, cars obediently pulling off to the side the moment the sirens announce them in the vicinity.

Her thoughts veer from anger to pure, mind-numbing worry. She clutches her phone in her hand, waiting for some sort of signal that Robin has been found. Her calls continue to go unanswered. She imagines the worst.

In the office, Jess had explained her findings to Freya. Patiently talking through what Robin had asked her to do, his theory about what had happened. Freya dug out the evidence bags from the cupboard, located the photograph that Robin had found. The Five, sitting on the steps of the beach hut, smiling. Sam, with his arm around Sara. And Meg nestled into Mike's chest. She'd gone through the rest of the photos and, sure enough, there they were. They weren't as obvious as Sara and Sam, but the embraces, the hugs she had assumed were platonic. They were together.

And Meg Carlton is pregnant. She'd brought the hip flask to the beach that night in order to maintain the illusion she was drinking. Robin had asked Jess for a blood test to confirm it. They had no authority to run it, and besides, what did it prove? But Jess had patiently explained the results from the tapings.

Alex's jumper found with fibres from Meg's pink scarf. A scarf Meg had tried to dispose of in the charity bin – a woman too obsessed with the environment to burn it like any good criminal should. And navy-blue paint fragments on Meg's scarf. Paint they all now know came from the beach hut.

And, with abrupt clarity, Freya knew where Robin had gone. His theory – that posting that news item in the paper would stir them up – had worked in more ways than one. Robin was hoping Meg would return to wherever she had stashed something incriminating.

She called Control, requesting multiple cars on scene. To the beach hut. Where she hoped, prayed, wished, that Robin would be there with Meg in cuffs. Where his phone would be broken, or out of signal. Any other reason why he wasn't answering. Just not that one. Please, not that.

She has commandeered one of the patrol cars to take her down there, but before she arrives, the message comes over the radio, loud and clear.

'Officer down! Officer down! Request ambulance immediately. Officer is unconscious, minimal breath sounds. State nine with one for attempted murder. I need a van please – all in order at this time.'

The officer driving requests clarification.

'Confirm which officer is down?'

Her shaking hands cover her mouth, and she leans forward, still, waiting for an answer.

'Confirming DS Robin Butler.'

The words rip the breath from her lungs. It's her fault. She should have been there, with him. It was her selfishness that caused their rift, her fault he had gone there alone.

The patrol car screeches into the car park; Freya jumps out before the vehicle has fully come to a stop. But to no avail. There's nobody there, except for a single uniformed cop.

She garbles a question to him. Tries again – and makes more sense this time.

'The ambulance has been and gone,' the officer replies. 'Taken DS Butler to the General. He was unconscious when they left.'

'Did they say anything else?'

'No, sorry. But your offender is still here. In cuffs, round the side. We're waiting for the van while we secure the scene.'

Freya looks in the direction the officer is pointing. She makes her way round, her slow footsteps trudging over the pebbles.

Dusk is starting to close in. Darkness settles around the beach huts, shadows growing longer as she walks. She hasn't been here before, but now she sees the navy beach hut, the backdrop to the photo. A cop slowly weaves crime scene tape around. Behind her she hears the arrival of the police van. Ahead, Megan Carlton stands with a uniformed officer, her hands in cuffs, her head bent to the ground.

She looks up as Freya approaches.

'I didn't mean to... Is he okay?' she babbles.

'We don't know yet,' Freya says, numbly. Meg looks a state. Her hair is a mess, her face puffy and red. Freya points to the car park.

'You can take her away now,' she addresses to the cop. 'The van's here.'

The officer starts to lead her away. 'What happens now?' Meg cries. 'Where am I going?'

But Freya doesn't answer. She walks over to the beach hut, stands outside the blue-and-white tape. The door is open. A trail of something dark leads inside. Freya's transfixed, motionless. Paralysed by the shame and guilt.

She stands, stunned, staring at the blood.

Robin's blood, on the wooden slats of the floor.

80

Tuesday

Freya sits with her head in her hands. She shifts, fidgeting, unable to stay still. She's been here all night, waiting. For news. For anything. For the doctors to come and find her.

Jess and her team arrived soon after Meg was driven away.

'Go to the hospital, Freya,' Jess said, gently. 'Josh and Mina will deal with Meg Carlton at the station. I'll get started here.'

A patrol car took her. Baker was already there. 'He's gone for a scan,' he said.

But still, they wait. Liam arrives, sits next to her, his face pale. Overnight, lights are dimmed, staff changed over. Offers of food, water, but Freya shakes her head no. The ache in the pit of her stomach won't go away. A pain left by the fear that Robin won't survive.

At one a.m. a doctor comes in.

'Robin received a considerable blow to the back of the head. The CT shows a small skull fracture, as well as a bleed to the brain. He's still unconscious in the ICU. We're continuing to observe his condition, and we'll know more over the next few hours.'

They thank him, useless platitudes in the wake of such awful news. Liam dozes, upright, his long body stretched across a few chairs, but Freya can't sleep. She blames herself. If they hadn't argued, Robin wouldn't have been alone. Stupid stubborn bugger, going out there by himself. Why hadn't he called her? Why hadn't he told her what he was doing?

Josh phones, updates her on the case. Megan Carlton has been charged with attempted murder for Robin's attack. She is in custody, pending questioning for the murder of Alex Reynolds. Sara has been released. That's one thing Freya is glad about.

In the morning, the hospital comes to life. The bustle increases, the smell of overcooked eggs encroaches on the pervading smell of disinfectant.

The door opens. Liam jerks awake, sitting up and rubbing his eyes. A doctor stands in front of them. He smiles.

'He's awake,' he says. 'And he'd like to see you.'

81

Robin has concluded that the less he moves, the better. Any shift of his head and a shard of fire races through his skull, making him want to puke. He blinks as doctors fire questions at his confused brain. They make him stare into a light, check him for all number of things he tries not to think about.

Eventually, he croaks, 'Is anyone here?'

A nurse smiles. 'Your brother-in-law. I'll get him. Just keep it short. You're still not well.'

Tell me about it, Robin thinks, as he swallows down a fresh wave of nausea.

When he opens his eyes again, Liam is there. He smiles at him, but Robin can see the worry, the lack of sleep etched on his red-raw eyes.

'You need to take better care of yourself,' he says. 'I can't lose you all.'

'I'm sorry, Liam.'

Liam reaches forward to give him a hug, then thinks better of it and grabs his hand instead. It's not something Robin's used to – this close contact, this reassurance – but he instantly relaxes.

'We've been here all night. Waiting to hear that you're okay.'

'We?'

'Me and Freya.' Liam smiles. 'She's been a mess.'

'Where is she now?' The thought that Freya is close by is soothing. He closes his eyes, feeling whatever drugs in his system take hold.

'Gone to make a call. She said Baker ordered her to phone the station the second you were in the clear.'

Am I? he thinks. He still doesn't feel great. The tiredness overwhelms him again and he closes his eyes. He feels Liam squeeze his hand tight.

'Tell her how you feel, mate,' he hears Liam say. 'Life's too short.'

82

Freya lingers in the corridor outside Robin's hospital ward.

'Hon, are you okay?' A nurse appears, concern apparent on her face.

'Yes, yes. I'm just… looking for Robin Butler.'

The nurse points into the room next to where Freya is standing.

'Yes, I know,' Freya tries to laugh but it comes out weird. 'It's… I don't know.' The nurse looks sympathetic, and it makes Freya start to cry.

'Oh, honey,' the nurse says. She gives Freya's arm a quick squeeze. 'You know he's going to be okay, right? A nasty bump on the head, but he'll be as right as rain.'

'Thank you,' Freya nods to the nurse, and she leaves, with another quick pat of the arm. Freya wipes her eyes. Stupid reaction, she tells herself. He's fine. *Fine*. She takes a deep breath and heads inside.

Robin's a few beds down, the lighting low. The curtains are open and as she approaches, she can see he's sat up slightly, resting on a few pillows, his eyes closed. She pauses by the bed, debating whether to wake him.

The head wound has been closed up, a white dressing over the top. Tufts of hair stick out next to a patch where it's been shaved. She looks at it, feeling a bubble of different emotions. Anger, at him, for going there alone.

Guilt for herself, for not being there. And a few other strange ones she finds hard to pin down. Fear, definitely. And a desperation, the absolute panic when she thought she would lose him.

It had felt similar to when Jonathan had died. The clawing loss at her insides. The helplessness, the empty void. But she'd been in love with Jonathan, hadn't she? And Robin, that's not… that's not it at all.

'Can you stop staring? It's weird.' Robin has half opened his eyes and is looking at her. 'Are you okay?' he asks. His voice is quiet and croaky.

'Yes, yes.'

'Then sit down, for fuck's sake.'

Freya does as she's told. 'How are you?' she asks.

'One hell of a headache. Turns out being hit with a lump of wood isn't that great for the brain.'

Freya feels herself about to cry again.

'Hey, hey,' Robin says. Without moving his head, he reaches out his hand. It's an odd gesture, coming from Robin, but she takes it. It's reassuringly warm. 'Enough of that. I'm fine.'

'But you might not have been. You might have been killed, Robin.' She's annoyed and pulls away. 'Why didn't you call me? Why did you just drive out there, by yourself?'

'Don't shout.'

'Seriously, Robin. You stupid man.'

'I know. And I'm sorry. I didn't mean to worry you.'

'I wasn't worried.'

'No?'

'Maybe a little bit. You were right, though. About Meg.'

'She's confessed?' He tries to sit forward in his bed, but closes his eyes with a wince and lies back again.

'Yep. All on tape. How she drugged Alex.'

'And what about Kevin Gillis?'

Freya shakes her head. 'Nothing. She refuses to talk about that. We'll keep trying, of course, but she seems shut up tight. Won't go down that route. We're still searching the beach hut, though. Who knows what we'll find.'

'Might even track down the knife,' Robin says.

'Let's hope,' she replies, although the words feel insincere. After everything Kevin Gillis did to Sara, maybe – and she doesn't like to say it out loud – maybe he deserved what he got. A knife in the chest feels justified.

Freya pauses. There's so much more to be said. 'And I'm sorry, Robin,' she blurts out. 'About everything we were arguing about. You were right. It was too much of a risk. I didn't tell him about Jonathan.'

Robin looks at her, silent, his brow furrowed.

'Please don't be angry with me, Robin.'

'I'm not,' he says softly. 'And it wasn't that I didn't want you to be happy. With Josh. With Optimus Prime.'

She smiles; the teasing is back. It's a good sign. 'I know,' she says.

'I was worried. I could never be angry with you, Freya. You and I. We're… You're my…' He stops. 'You know.'

'Best mate?' She can't help smiling.

'Something like that.'

'I am?'

'Well, at least top five. Stop smirking or I'll relegate you to top ten.'

'You don't have ten friends.'

'I'll make some more. Just to spite you.' He grins, and she smiles back. Then something seems to bother him.

'Do you remember that guy at the garage? Bert. With the Mini?' She nods. 'Is that how you'd describe me? Solid and dependable?'

'Don't forget safe,' she jokes. But, judging from the look on his face, it doesn't seem to be a portrayal that he likes.

'Am I really that dull?' he asks.

She pauses. She thinks about how different things have been since she met him, over a year ago. How much she enjoys going to work, how happy she is.

'Life with you has never been boring, Robin. I've missed you,' she adds, quietly.

'I've missed you, too.'

She pauses. 'In that case...' She thinks of the necklace she found in his desk drawer. 'Can I have my Christmas present?'

'Your... You found it?' He looks embarrassed as she nods. 'I'm sorry I didn't give it to you. It's... well. You'll see. As soon as we get back to the office.'

Now it's her turn to blush. 'I have it here. In my bag.'

'You nicked it out of my desk? Go on then.'

She takes it out of her bag, and rests it on the bed between them. She pulls out the tissue paper and the small box, trying hard to pretend she hasn't done it before. She opens it; she loves the tiny bee just as much as when she first saw it.

'I love it, Robin. Thank you so much.'

'You opened it already, didn't you?' he says, smiling.

'Yes,' she says, and he cackles again. 'But I couldn't resist, and I loved it. I wanted it!'

'You like it then? You don't think it's a bit...' He shrugs, squirming a little.

'A bit what?'

'Too much? For work colleagues.'

'But I'm top five, Robin,' she jokes. 'You said. Here. I'll put it on.'

She takes the necklace out of the box and puts it round her neck, lifting her hair out of the way and awkwardly fastening the clasp. 'There. How does it look?'

He smiles. 'Beautiful.'

He has a strange expression on his face. Like he's distracted, although his eyes are locked on hers. He looks like he's going to say something, but then his gaze shifts to the space behind her, and Freya turns.

There's another woman coming towards them. Someone she recognises. The woman smiles warmly.

'DC West,' she says. 'It's nice to see you again.'

'DI Craig. But what are you…?' Freya's confused. Last thing she knew, Craig and Robin hated each other.

'Jo and I are… I don't know.' Robin looks self-conscious again.

'It's early days,' she replies. She smiles at him, then reaches down and kisses him on the cheek. 'We bumped into each other on New Year's Eve,' she directs to Freya.

'How did you know I was here?' Robin asks.

'I saw something on the news. A murder detective attacked in the course of his duties on a beach in Southampton. I knew it could only be you, getting into trouble. I phoned your nick.'

'Right! Okay!' Freya's voice feels unnaturally cheerful but there's nothing she can do to stop it. 'I'll go then,' she says, quickly. 'I'll come back and see you tomorrow, Robin. We'll go over the case, make sure I've covered everything in the paperwork.'

'Freya, you don't have to…' she hears Robin say, but she's already walking away. Fast out of the ward, down the corridor, out of the hospital. She's out of breath and she stops, leaning against a wall.

Cold wind whips round the building. What was she thinking? That her and Robin were... what? More than friends? Her hand goes to the silver bee round her neck, her fingers running it up and down the delicate chain.

He doesn't see you like that, she tells herself. Don't be so stupid. And you have Josh. Your wonderful boyfriend Josh, who wants to be with you, and live with you. What the hell are you thinking?

She shakes her head, trying to dispel the sinking feeling in her stomach. She doesn't have *feelings* for Robin Butler, she tells herself. Don't be so ridiculous. He's grumpy, and uncommunicative, and depressed. The complete opposite of Josh in every way.

She starts walking again. Long, fast strides towards the main road. This case, this whole case, has messed with her mind. She'll be glad when it's over and things can go back to normal.

She'll phone Josh. He can pick her up. Take her home. She can get some sleep. Eat something. But she doesn't call.

The walking is helping. Putting life into her bones, energy into her body. It's just because you thought Robin might die, she tells herself as she thrusts her freezing hands into her coat pockets. You were worried you would lose him. That's all. She marches faster. That's all.

And so she walks. She walks. Trying to quash the strange feeling about Robin, churning in her insides.

83

The phone rings. Sara jumps.

She's been sat waiting, all day. She lifts the receiver and he's there.

'Sam! Are you okay?'

'I'm fine.' A pause. 'They've charged me with his murder, Sara.'

'But… but…' It's ridiculous. He didn't… She can't believe it.

'I can't say much. They're listening.'

All these years, and it comes down to this. Sam locked away. For the murder of a man who deserved it.

In the hours, the days after the rape, Sara imagined going back there. A knife in her hand. A rope. Drugs, even. Anything to make him pay. The rage, the anger was pure. She wanted to kill him.

And then he disappeared, and the pub closed. The five of them sat mute in their living room, waiting. For what? The newspapers were silent. The knock on the door never came.

And the agreement – they had got away with it. But they would never speak again.

'Your lawyers,' she says. 'They'll get you out, won't they?'

'They're trying. But this is murder. They said not to expect bail.' Sam's voice is slow, hard, quiet. 'They're keeping me in tonight. The court hearing is tomorrow. We'll know more then.'

'They've charged Meg with Alex's murder. And attempted murder on that police officer.'

'I heard.'

'Do you know why she—'

'Sara, I have to go. They don't give you long.' He pauses. She hears a noise, and with a jolt she realises he's crying. 'I'm sorry, Sara,' he says, his voice thick with emotion.

She's stunned. 'Why are you sorry?'

'Because… because I couldn't be there for you. After you were attacked. I know I was useless. I know I said the wrong things, messed everything up between us.'

'Sam, it's not—'

'It was.' He sniffs again. Sara's not used to this vulnerability from Sam. His usual confidence, the bravado, it's gone. 'I know something more happened that night, that you didn't want to tell me about. But I should have… I should have… Everything I've done since – my doctorates, training as a therapist – it was for you. To help you. So I could make up for the mistakes I made then.' There's a beep on the line. A noise announcing the imminent end of the call. 'I love you, Sara.'

'I love you, too. Sam—?'

But he's gone. The line is dead.

She sinks to the floor. Kevin Gillis has ruined her life. Again. Once when he raped her, and again now, taking the man she loves. Her brain races, trying to think of a way out. They should have run before. Taken the kids and left. But they had got away with it for so long.

Until now.

84

Robin can't stay awake for long. He finds himself hitting pockets of sleepiness, dipping in and out of the world. He loses track of time. The drugs help.

Liam comes and goes. At one point he opens his eyes and it's dark, the hospital quiet. Liam is sat next to his bed, reading, a pair of glasses perched on his nose. His legs are crossed, one foot resting on the edge of the bed. Without looking away from his book, he reaches across and helps himself to the open box of chocolates next to him. Robin stays silent. They've been clearly left for him, but Liam's helping himself without hesitation. It elicits a feeling in Robin. One he hasn't felt for a while. Belonging. Love. Family. He closes his eyes again, listening to Liam's breathing and the flutter of a page being turned.

He sleeps. He dreams. He exists in states between the two – the opiates, his recovering brain, meaning he doesn't stay long in either. The case flickers through his mind. The faces of The Five. Green gates, locked tight. A hole in a car park, a red digger. Sara – with Sam, with Mike. A dead body crammed in a car. Images that don't make sense. Images he lets go.

When he wakes again, it seems to be morning. Hazy sunlight filters through the dirty windows. He feels marginally better. Hungry, even.

He lifts his head and slowly reaches towards the jug of water on his bedside table.

'Here. I'll get that.' Jo appears in the doorway. She smiles. 'You're awake.'

He nods, wincing as a fresh ache squeezes his skull. Not so good after all.

'How long have I been out?' he says, his throat hoarse. He feels like his voice hasn't been used in a while.

'A few days,' Jo replies. She hands him a cup of water and sits down next to him. He sips it tentatively. It helps.

'Liam's popped home for a bit. Freya's been in and out. I said I'd keep an eye on you.'

'In case I do what?' he says. 'Disappear?'

'You have form,' she replies, and he smiles. Then she looks unsure. 'I hope you don't mind me being here.'

'No, not at all. Although I'm not at my best.' Robin has no idea how he looks right now. But he's sure that a bash over the head and a few days in bed won't have done him any favours.

'You can make an effort when we go out. Later.'

He stays silent, watching her. He finds it odd, this new person in his life. Thrown in so unexpectedly. He likes her, hopes it could be something.

The look on her face is turning uncertain in light of his pause.

'I would like that,' he says slowly.

She tilts her head to one side. 'But?' she pre-empts.

'But.' He smiles softly. 'I've not had the greatest track record. With relationships. And I'm not sure what the best thing to do is. I like you, Jo,' he adds, and she returns his smile. 'And I don't want to mess this up.'

'Is there someone else?' she asks, and he quickly shakes his head. The movement makes his brain rattle and he closes his eyes for a second.

'But there was,' he manages at last, thinking about Steph. 'Sort of. I fucked that up by… by being useless. Non-committal. And I don't want you to get the wrong idea about me.'

'What's the right idea?'

'That I like you. A lot. But I've got shit in my past, bad stuff, that means I'm not as…' He pauses, trying to find the right word. 'Functional. As I'd like to be,' he continues. 'I have problems with depression. Dealing with grief. I don't ask for help when I need it. I get really angry at the world, and I don't express it in a way that's healthy.'

He realises he's said too much. The drugs are clearly having an impact. But for once in his life, he wants to be honest. And he realises how Freya must have felt, wanting to tell Josh the truth.

He makes himself stop talking, then glances at Jo to see how she's taken the news. But she's not looking horrified or disgusted.

She leans forward and takes his hand. 'Do you know,' she says with a smile. 'That's probably the most honest any man has ever been with me. And we haven't even been out yet.'

'Oh, fuck,' he mumbles. 'I'm sorry. Blame the drugs. I should have kept my mouth shut.'

'No, no. It's good. And I like you, too, Robin. I like where this could go. If we stand any chance of a future together, then you need to be telling me stuff like this.'

He sighs. He's sure that you're supposed to try and impress someone at the beginning of a relationship. Not lie in bed in a hospital gown, with tubes going god knows where, and pour your heart out about your mental health issues.

'Listen,' she says. 'How about you recover, and once you're out of hospital, we open a bottle of wine and I can tell you all the myriad of ways I'm fucked up. That will make you feel better. Deal?'

'Deal.'

Jo stands up. 'Now, I have to head to work. These murders aren't going to solve themselves.'

She leans forward and kisses him softly. It's brief, on the cheek, but her hair grazes his face and he catches a brief waft of her perfume.

Liam appears in the doorway behind them. He waits as Jo picks up her bag and says her goodbyes.

'I'll be back soon,' she says, and with a last brief smile over her shoulder, she leaves.

Liam watches her go. 'She was unexpected,' he says, sitting down next to Robin's bed. 'How are you feeling?'

'Better,' Robin replies.

He has a mug of takeaway coffee in his hand, and the smell fills the room, making Robin nostalgic for the office. For getting out of here and restarting his life. 'Have you seen Freya?' he asks.

'Briefly. She said to tell you she's still on the case. And she wants to talk to you.' Robin opens his mouth but Liam stops him. 'I won't let you. You're ill.'

'This afternoon,' Robin bargains.

'Tomorrow. At the earliest. Now, do you want some food? Doctor gave the all-clear if you're up for it.'

Robin agrees and Liam heads out into the corridor.

Robin lies back on his pillow. He raises a hand to the back of his head, tentatively exploring the bandage and the stitches underneath. Strange how things work out.

A bump on the head, and suddenly he has the start of a new relationship with Jo. The potential of something, someone, that could work.

He thinks about Freya, and the feelings that have been growing for months. Ridiculous, impossible emotions. They're friends, partners. No more. Every day he gets to see Freya, work cases with her. Hear whatever peculiar thoughts are going through her mind. It's enough. What more could he possibly need?

He closes his eyes. He thinks of the people around him. Who care. Who love him. And for the first time in months, he feels a flicker of contentment. He's vaguely aware of footsteps as Liam comes back into the room.

'Food's on its way, mate,' Liam says. 'Be about half an hour. You have a kip.'

His brother-in-law slumps back into the chair, then hooks one long leg over the arm as he opens his book again. Robin hears the rustle of the chocolate box. He thinks of Freya back at the nick, trying to wrestle a confession out of Meg Carlton. Josh and Mina battling paperwork, cursing the mess on his desk as they document the exhibits. Their faces, the people in his life that he loves. Yes, even Josh – even Boy Wonder has his good side.

A world, his life, that for the first time in years he is happy to go back to.

He lets his mind wander. The pieces fade. And for a moment, one perfect moment, he lives in that wonderful fragment of happiness.

Epilogue

It never grows dark at the hospital. It never gets quiet. Mike is used to the noise now: the beep of monitors, the gossip between nurses, the squeak of Crocs on a newly cleaned floor. He knows they're going to release him soon. Back home to recover. To Sara and the kids.

He looks forward to that. A normality, as temporary as he knows it will be. This past month has been hell. He barely slept after Alex told him his plans to go to the police; all the events from twenty years before, rushing up to meet him.

He hears footsteps in the corridor. Slow, steady. A dark figure appears in the doorway.

He can just see his face in the low lighting. It's that cop. The detective – Butler. He looks strange, a patch of his hair shaved on one side, dark stitches visible on his scalp. This must be the one Meg attacked, he thinks. He's wearing slippers, tracksuit trousers and a black T-shirt, but his manner is formal.

'I'm sorry,' the cop says.

Mike nods, accepting the apology. There's a pause; a woman joins the detective in the doorway. The blonde one he met before. DC West.

Mike clears his throat. 'You know, don't you?'

The man nods.

'How?'

'Something didn't add up. Sam couldn't have done it alone.'

'We know why you did it.' The woman is talking now. Like the man, she looks apologetic, like she doesn't want to be there. 'For Sara.'

Mike nods. 'He couldn't get away with it. What he did to her.'

–

He hadn't expected the blood. The slick of warmth on his hands when he pushed the knife in. The expression on Kevin Gillis's face: the mocking, jeering, turning to surprise. He hadn't intended to kill.

He only went to the pub to confront him. Sara begged him to leave it alone, but anger overtook all rational thought.

He'd known something was wrong, from the second they came home that night. Meg's face was pale as she told them.

Sara said he hit her. Choked her. Groped her a bit. But Mike knew it was more than that. She wouldn't let anyone near her. Flinching at the slightest touch. Eventually, he managed to give her a hug, wrapping his arms around her in silence as she sobbed.

'What's wrong? What's wrong?' he asked her repeatedly, but she shook her head and pulled away.

She went to bed with Sam. He heard her crying through the walls, his room next to hers. But in the morning, she wasn't any better. She refused to go out, said she didn't feel like eating. Days passed, and she got thinner, quieter. He thought about calling her parents, but he knew she wouldn't want that. And then a few days later, he heard a quiet tap on his door. She came inside, standing, uncertain, next to his bed, her arms wrapped round her body. The lights were off, the house quiet, and he felt her climb into bed next to him.

'I have to do this,' she whispered. 'To make it better.'

'Have to do what?' he replied, confused. But she kissed him, hard. He responded. She pulled him on top of her. But as he reached for a condom, he realised she was crying.

'No, carry on,' she pleaded when he stopped. 'Sam's too scared to touch me. I need to do this. Please.'

But she couldn't stop crying. He rolled to her side, pulling her close, stroking her hair. 'What happened?' he asked.

And then she said it.

'He raped me. Kevin. At the bar.'

'You have to tell the police,' he said. But she shook her head furiously.

'No one will believe me. Not now. It's all gone. The proof.' She turned to him in the darkness. 'Don't tell them, please. None of them know. Not even Sam.'

She'd looked so beautiful the night of their grad ball. Her new short hair suited her, her dress made her sparkle. But she had left early; the bruises on her neck were visible under the make-up, the psychological scars only just making themselves known.

The others had stayed. Even Sam, who was still supposedly her boyfriend. Mike crept away. Back home, where she was already sleeping, the open box of pills next to her. He crouched to the side of her bed, and gently moved a strand of hair away from her face. Another man had kissed her mouth. Another man had grabbed her breasts. Another man had— His brain shut down at the thought.

The feelings that ripped through his body were nothing he'd ever experienced before. Anger, sadness, jealousy and, yes, even a bit of blame. Why had she put herself in that position? Alone, with him? And how dare he? How. Dare. He.

That man destroyed her. He'd taken what he wanted. With the emasculating knowledge that Mike had done nothing.

The anger swelled. The rage, the hatred, filled him.

The others were out; there had been nobody there to stop him as he stormed out of the house, down the road towards the pub.

Kevin had been alone. Wiping down the bar, all punters gone for the night.

'We're closed, mate,' he said as Mike walked in. Then he recognised him, from the fight the fortnight before. His face clouded. 'What do you want?'

'To talk to you.'

'You're banned. You and your mates. Although Sara can come back, if she wants.' He leered then, as if he'd had a thought he found funny 'I like Sara. She can stay for as long as she likes.'

'You stay away from Sara.'

'Says who? You? You're with her now, are you?'

He took a few steps towards the bar. Gillis didn't move.

'You need to admit what you did.'

A curl of the lip. 'What?'

'You and Sara. That you...' But he couldn't say it. The words stuck in his throat.

'Fucked her?' he mocked.

'You raped her!'

The words flew from his mouth like vomit. His whole body throbbed with rage.

'That's what she told you, is it? That I raped her?' Kevin scoffed with derision. 'She was into it. She let me. You try and prove otherwise.'

Mike took two more steps. Behind the bar now.

'So she regrets it now?' Gillis said. He slowly reversed into the doorway of the kitchen, seemingly keen to keep distance between them. 'Silly drunk bitch. And you're even more stupid to believe her. She lay there, wanted me to do it.'

Two more steps. Both of them now in the kitchen. And Mike saw the knife.

Large. Long. Used for slicing lemons for the cocktails. It glinted in the light, sharp and ready.

'Admit you raped her,' Mike said again.

And Kevin Gillis laughed in his face. He fucking laughed.

Two more steps, the knife in his hand. One more: in Kevin's chest.

He wasn't a big guy. He didn't put up much of a fight once Mike was upon him. He doesn't remember the actual stabbing, just the feeling of warm, thick liquid, then the panic as Kevin collapsed. Mike looked disbelieving at the knife in his hand, slippery with blood, the tip missing. He dropped it with a clatter, then stood, staring.

He must have stayed there for a while. Watching, as the man died in front of him. Because when he came to, he was cold, the blood dried to a paste. Coating him from his fingertips to the elbows of his formal white dress shirt.

He took two steps to the phone. Picked it up and dialled. Alex answered.

'I need a lawyer,' Mike said.

'What have you done?'

'I'm at the pub.'

And they arrived. The three of them: Meg, Alex and Sam.

All of them stood, pale, staring at the man on the floor.

'What the fuck did you do, Mike?' Alex stuttered. Meg wordlessly bent down and put two fingers on his neck.

'He's dead,' she said.

'Well, yeah,' Sam mocked in reply.

'We need to call the police.'

Mike looked at them all, terrified. 'I can't go to prison. I can't.'

'Then we bury the body,' Alex replied.

Mike was surprised at his calm. His composure. Alex turned to them all.

'Look at us,' he said. 'Look where we're standing.'

They all looked down. Blood had spread across the entire floor of the small kitchen, soaking into their shoes. Meg's trainers, strange in contrast to her formal ball dress, obviously put on quickly when they ran from the house. Alex's and Sam's smart shoes, like his. Black trousers, white shirts, black dinner jackets.

There would be splashes up their legs where they had walked through, spatters on their skin. Mike could see red streaks on Meg's hands where she'd taken his pulse.

'You could say it was self-defence,' Meg stuttered. 'That he went for you.'

'The police won't believe it,' Alex replied. 'They'll think we're all involved. And even if there's a trial, and we're found innocent, that will be the end of all our lives. You – Sam. You want to be a shrink. Me, a lawyer. You want to be a teacher, Meg. And Mike's going to be a cop.

A cop! No one is going to let us have those careers, not with accusations like this hanging over our heads.'

There was no mention of Mike confessing. No question why Mike had done it. They knew. They would stick together. The Five.

They all looked at each other. They were twenty-one, had their whole lives ahead of them. They nodded.

'How do we do this?' Mike replied.

-

Nobody saw them. Nobody even suspected. Sam fetched his car. They rolled the body in the lino and awkwardly bundled it inside. They all sat still, cocooned in their living room, silent, on Monday, for news that the body had been found. But nothing. Alex returned from work dirty, tired, and he nodded.

'It's gone,' he said. 'Buried.'

Under a foot of concrete. Nobody would ever find Kevin Gillis.

But twenty years later, they had.

In his hospital bed, Mike flexes his hand, almost relishing the agony that races through his damaged nerve endings. This is retribution. Although, it wasn't much. Not when you consider what he'd done.

'Meg had the code to the gates,' Butler says. 'Alex worked on the roads, he knew the renovation was being done to the car park.'

Mike nods. 'Where was the knife?' he asks.

The one thing he'd worried about all this time. The knife with his fingerprints. They couldn't find it after the body had gone.

But the detective replies, 'Meg had it.'

Mike looks down. Of course. Fucking Meg. She'd never got over him. He'd taken advantage, that day a few months ago when they'd slept together. When he needed reassurance that despite Sara's affair, he was still attractive. He was still loved. By someone.

'She kept it. At the beach hut. That's how we knew. By killing Alex, Meg was protecting you. The man she loves.' Butler pauses, glances across to West. 'We found traces of Kevin Gillis's blood in a drawer.'

Mike's head snaps up. 'Traces of blood?'

'We don't have it,' he replies. 'It's gone.'

The two detectives pause. They make no move to arrest him, no attempt to read him the caution. He knows what they're saying. *We have nothing on you. We know you killed him; we know why. And we understand.*

'What about Sam?' he asks slowly.

'He's pleaded guilty to preventing the lawful burial of a body,' Butler says. 'He's out.'

'You let him go?'

'For now. Until his sentencing, whenever that is. He says they found the body. Him and Alex. And they buried it because they worried it would incriminate them.'

'And you believe him?'

'We have nothing to prove otherwise.' A quick glance to West. A nod of agreement.

'It's over,' she says.

They leave. It's over. The words rattle in his head. It's over. They know, and it's over.

But he still doesn't let himself breathe.

One thing is for sure: he took someone's life. The blood on his hands. At night when he can't sleep, he sees it, he feels it. Warm and wet, spilling to the floor. Draining from the man he killed.

It never grows dark.
It never gets quiet.
He never forgets.

Acknowledgements

Twenty years ago, I was lucky to go to Southampton University with a truly wonderful group of people, and even luckier that I still count them among my best friends today. This book is dedicated to the residents of 28 Shakespeare Avenue, both unofficial and official. So, to Anne, Beef, Div, Meenal, Nikki, Seetal and Sue, thank you.

Thank you to everyone at Canelo Crime, but especially Louise Cullen, my editor, for ripping apart the manuscript without breaking my heart, as only she knows how. Thank you to Daniela Nava for the copy-editing, and Jenny Page for the proofreading. Who knows how many errors there would be if it wasn't for you both.

Thank you to my magnificent agent, Ed Wilson, and all the team at Johnson and Alcock.

As always, a huge thank you to Dr Matt Evans. Matt invests so much of his spare time making sure I get the medical side of everything correct, answering my queries in between a busy consultant's job and a very small baby. I am forever in his debt.

In the same vein, thank you to PC Dan Roberts and Charlie Roberts for allowing me to take up so much of their spare time on my gormless questions about police detail and procedure.

My psychology knowledge is rusty, so thank you to Dr Chris Stiff and Dr Ben Gardner-Sood for your help with Dr Sam Bowen.

Thank you to James Burford, for providing insights into Alex's office and the legal side of things, and Susan Scarr for everything pharmacological. Thank you to Stephanie Fox, my forensic expert, and Laura Stevenson, because it's always handy to have a paramedic around.

Thank you to everyone from the Criminal Minds group. I consider myself immeasurably fortunate for being introduced to you all at a time when the pandemic had made a writer's life especially lonely. So, thank you to Niki, for the introduction, and to Dom, Tim, Jo, Heather, Elle, Victoria, Rachael, Fliss, Rob, Barry, Adam, Liz, Susie, Harriet, Phoebe, Clare, Kate and Polly – thank you for the support in this insane profession. Infinite llamas, jellyfish, and pincers up for you all.

Finally, to my family – to Chris and Ben, to Mum and Dad, and Tom and Mel – thank you. I couldn't do it without you.

Do you love crime fiction and are always on the lookout for brilliant authors?

Canelo Crime is home to some of the most exciting novels around. Thousands of readers are already enjoying our compulsive stories. Are you ready to find your new favourite writer?

Find out more and sign up to our newsletter at canelocrime.com